Other titles of interest from Macmillan

Hull & John: *Non-destructive Testing*
John: *Introduction to Engineering Materials, 2nd edition*
Hall: *Polymer Materials, 2nd edition*
John: *Engineering Materials (College Work Out)*
Ryder: *Strength of Materials*

TESTING OF MATERIALS

VERNON JOHN

MACMILLAN

First published 1992 by
MACMILLAN EDUCATION LTD
Houndmills, Basingstoke, Hampshire RG21 2XS
and London
Companies and representatives
throughout the world

Typeset by
TecSet Ltd, Wallington, Surrey

ISBN 0–333–56814–1 hardcover
ISBN 0–333–44783–2 paperback

A catalogue record for this book is available from
the British Library

Printed in Hong Kong

Contents

Note on standards

The majority of testing methods for material properties are standardised. Each major country possesses its own standards institutions. The standards for a particular test procedure, for example the testing of metals in tension, will be similar from one country to another but may differ on some points of detail such as the specific dimensions of test pieces. In general, references in the text are made to British Standards but in some cases, where there is no appropriate British Standard, an ASTM (American) standard is quoted. A list of relevant British and American standards is given in the Appendix. Extracts from British Standards are reproduced by permission of BSI. (Complete copies of the standards can be obtained from them at Linford Wood, Milton Keynes, MK14 6LE.)

Acknowledgements

I would like to thank Harry Beasley for the time and effort he put in to produce the photographic illustrations for this book. I would like also to thank my wife, Gillian, for her full support throughout the preparation of this text and for converting my barely legible scrawl into type.

Vernon John

1
The Requirements for Testing

1.1 Introduction

Testing is an essential part of any engineering activity. Inspection and testing must take place at many stages in the complex process of producing engineering materials, be they metals, polymers, ceramics or composites, and during the forming of these materials into components and assembling the components to create an engineering product to satisfy some specific requirement. The requirement for testing does not automatically cease when the product has been manufactured. It is frequently necessary to check and test the article during its service life in order to monitor changes, such as the possible development of fatigue or corrosion damage.

The types of test used can be broadly classified into two categories

(a) tests to establish the properties of the material, and
(b) tests to determine the integrity of the material or component.

Those tests in the first category are generally of a destructive type. They are performed on samples of a material and the test-piece is damaged or broken in the process, as is the case when determining the tensile strength of a material in a tensile test to destruction. If the sample test-piece is correctly chosen and prepared the results should be indicative of the properties of the bulk material represented by the sample.

The tests in the second category are of a non-destructive nature and are used to detect the presence of internal or surface flaws in a material, component or finished product. By their very nature, these tests do not damage the parts being tested and sampling is not required as, if necessary, every item can be checked.

1.2 The Need for Testing

Testing is necessary at many points in the engineering process.

(a) As a quality control check in the production of metal semi-finished products, for example sheet, strip, bar stock, etc. Sample destructive property tests are made to ensure that the material can meet the appropriate specification. Non-destructive tests may also be made at this stage to ensure that the product is defect-free.

(b) As an acceptance check by a component manufacturer to ensure that the material will give the required performance. Again this will generally involve sample destructive property tests.

(c) To check finished components prior to final assembly. Non-destructive tests would be used for this purpose. It is also possible to use one form of non-destructive test, namely radiography, on some completed multi-component products to check for the correctness of assembly.

(d) For the in-service checking of components. Non-destructive tests are used here to detect deterioration or damage, for example the presence of corrosion or fatigue cracks.

In addition to the above, property testing of materials is widely used during research and development programmes and also for the compilation of general design data files.

It is of extreme importance that the user of materials be able to obtain reliable information on the properties of those materials. The range of properties which can be considered is extremely large, including strength in tension, compression and shear at ambient temperature and at temperatures other than ambient, stiffness, hardness, impact strength, time-dependent properties such as fatigue and creep phenomena, resistance to oxidation, corrosion and other forms of chemical and microbial attack. It would be extremely expensive and time consuming to fully assess all of these characteristics for any one material and the engineer has to determine which are the properties of significance for the particular application being considered. In this context, it will be necessary for the engineer to determine not only that the material will possess the properties to enable it to give an adequate and reliable performance when in use but also that the material has those properties that will permit it to be readily fabricated into the required shape and form.

The test procedures which have been devised for the determination of some of the characteristic properties of materials, for example the tensile test, will provide much valuable information for the engineer and designer but this data will not necessarily be sufficient to predict accurately how the material will behave when it is fabricated into some end product and put into service. The properties of a metallic material are dependent to some extent on the size and alignment of the crystal grains within the material. The grain structure of a manufactured component may differ from that in the test-piece used in the determination of the tensile properties. The properties of many thermoplastic materials are highly sensitive to changes in temperature and to variations in strain rate. The results obtained from tests on ceramics may show a large variance and a large number of tests may be necessary to show this variance and determine a statistical mean.

For the results of any test to have value, it is important that the tests be conducted according to certain set procedures. To this end, standardised test procedures have been evolved. In the United Kingdom, the British Standards Institution publishes the standards and codes of practice which cover most aspects of the testing and utilisation of materials. All the major developed countries possess standards organisations and while standards for a particular type of test may differ slightly on points of detail from one country to another, the broad principles will be similar. A list of British (BS) and American (ASTM) Standards relevant to the tests covered in this volume is given in the Appendix.

1.3 Material Property Tests

The material characteristics which are most often called for by the engineer and designer are the values of Young's Modulus, E, the tensile yield stress (or proof stress) and tensile strength, ductility and hardness. Dependent on the type of mechanical loading the material may be subject to in service, it may also be necessary to have information on the compressive and shear strengths of the material. Many components are subject to fluctuating loads or cyclic stressing, where the load on the component may rapidly alternate between compressive and tensile values. In this case, a knowledge of the fatigue characteristics of the material will be of great importance. Creep, which is the continued slow deformation of a material with time under conditions of constant load, is a phenomenon which becomes of importance for metallic materials when they are used at elevated temperatures. It should not be thought, though, that creep is only a high-temperature phenomenon, as many polymeric materials will creep at temperatures at or close to ambient values.

Many components are fabricated from sheet metal by plastic deformation processes such as bending, pressing, deep drawing and spinning, and a number of tests have been developed to assess the formability of sheet material.

The succeeding chapters of this book will give details of the various test procedures for determining the types of property listed above together with the manner of result presentation required and the ways in which the engineer would use test data. Many of the tests described conform to British Standards but there is also coverage of some test methods which are commonly used but for which there is no relevant standard.

1.4 Non-destructive Testing

As mentioned above, the materials property data derived from standard destructive tests do not necessarily give a clear guide to the performance characteristics of components which may form part of some larger engineering assembly. Defects of various types and sizes may be introduced to a material or component during manufacture and the exact nature and size of any defect may influence the subsequent performance of the component. Other defects, such as fatigue or corrosion cracks, may be generated within a component during service. It is necessary to have reliable means for detecting the presence of defects at the manufacturing stage and also for detecting and monitoring the rate of growth of defects during the service life of a component or assembly. Using well established physical principles a number of testing systems have been developed which will provide information on the quality of a material or component and which do not alter or damage the components or assemblies which are tested. The main non-destructive systems which are used are

(a) liquid penetrant inspection,
(b) magnetic particle inspection,
(c) electrical (eddy current) testing,
(d) ultrasonic testing, and
(e) radiography,

Correct and effective use of non-destructive testing will result in the identification of defects which, if they remained undetected, could result in a catastrophic failure. This could prove to be very costly in financial terms and possibly in lives and so effective use of suitable inspection techniques could give rise to substantial savings.

These main non-destructive testing techniques are described in Chapter 8 of this book, together with some of the major areas of application for the various tests.

2
Hardness and its Measurement

2.1 The Property of Hardness

The property of hardness is not a fundamental property of a material. The term *hardness* may be defined in more than one way. It may be regarded as the resistance of the material to abrasion, or as the resistance to localised plastic deformation. The various types of hardness test which have been devised are based on the measurement of one or other of these characteristics of a material. The test types which involve localised plastic deformation can, of course, only be used in connection with those materials which are capable of being deformed plastically, namely metals and thermoplastics. These tests are indentation-type tests and may be either static or dynamic. In the static indentation tests, which are the more commonly used, an indentation is made in the surface of the material under a pre-determined load and the size of the indentation measured. The larger an indentation is, when made under standard conditions, the softer is the material, and vice versa. Although indentation tests do not measure the resistance to abrasion, in general, a material of high hardness, as determined by an indentation method, will possess a good resistance to abrasion and wear. Dynamic indentation tests involve a free falling weight or a pendulum impacting with a material. Some of the energy of the striker will be absorbed in causing some plastic deformation of the material while the remainder of the impact energy will remain in the striker causing it to rebound. A hard material will not absorb much energy, as it will not greatly deform plastically, so giving a large striker rebound height. This type of test is particularly suited to extremely hard metals. This type of test is also used for assessing a group of materials which are not usually considered as being very hard materials, namely rubbers. An indentor will cause both elastic and plastic deformation. When the striker in a dynamic test impacts with a rubber, the very rapid rate of elastic strain recovery of the rubber will cause the rebound height of the striker to be great. Despite this apparent anomaly of a soft material giving a large rebound value indicating a high hardness, this type of test is used successfully to assess the properties of rubber-type materials. It is possible also to measure the hardness of steels using an electrical non-contact method. The parameter which is measured is magnetic coercivity but, for each particular type of steel, there is an almost linear relationship between coercivity and hardness.

Indentation-type hardness tests are widely used to check metal samples. The tests are relatively easy to make and do not require elaborately machined test-pieces. The results of the tests will give an indication of the strength of a metal — there are certain empirical relationships between hardness value and tensile strength for a number of metallic materials — and the results of hardness tests can also be a convenient way of checking on the effectiveness of heat treatments.

There are some materials, notably ceramics and glasses, which do not deform plastically when a force is applied and indentation type hardness tests cannot be used for these. For this type of material, the only suitable type of hardness test is one which measures the resistance to abrasion. One such test, and the one most usually used, is Mohs' scale of hardness.

2.2 Mohs' Scale of Hardness

Mohs' scale of hardness was originally devised for assessing the relative hardnesses of rocks and minerals but is now also used for determining the relative hardnesses of industrial ceramic and glass materials. It is based on a set of ten naturally occurring minerals ranging from talc, which is very soft, to diamond, the hardest known substance. The full scale is given in Table 2.1. In this test, attempts are made to scratch the surfaces of the standards with the material which is being assessed. The hardness number of the unknown material lies between the number of the standard mineral which it just fails to scratch and that of the standard which it just scratches.

Table 2.1 Mohs' scale of hardness

Number	Mineral
1	talc
2	gypsum
3	calcite
4	fluorite
5	apatite
6	orthoclase felspar
7	quartz
8	topaz
9	corundum
10	diamond

Table 2.2 Recommended ratios of F/D^2 for the Brinell hardness test on various materials

Material	F/D^2
Steels and cast irons	30
Copper alloys and aluminium alloys	10
Pure copper and aluminium	5
Lead, tin and tin alloys	1

very small and the edge of the impression is ill-defined when viewed through a microscope, making it difficult to measure the diameter accurately. In the case of a deep indentation, the impression is clearly defined but, although the diameter can be measured accurately, a significant increase in the depth of indentation, and hence increase in the surface area of the impression, would not be reflected in a major change in the diameter, d. This, again, leads to a reduction in the accuracy with which the hardness can be

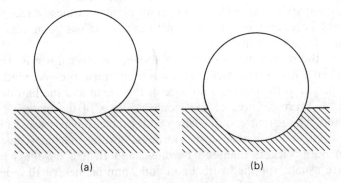

(a)   (b)

Figure 2.1 (a) Shallow impression, (b) Deep impression. The impressions are not geometrically similar and hence the plastic flow patterns within material differ.

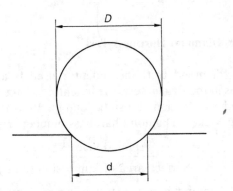

Figure 2.2 Diameter of impression, d, in relation to diameter of ball, D.

measured. For these reasons, accurate Brinell hardness values will only be achieved if the impression diameter, d, is between the limits of $0.25D$ and $0.5\,D$, where D is the diameter of the ball. The surface area of an impression of diameter, d, made by a spherical indentor of diameter, D, is given by

$$\text{Area} = \pi D/2 \left[D - \sqrt{(D^2 - d^2)} \right]$$

and so

$$H_B = \frac{2F}{\pi D [D - \sqrt{(D^2 - d^2)}]}$$

The Brinell test is not suitable for the testing of very hard materials. As the hardness of the metal approaches that of the ball indentor, there will be a tendency for the indentor to deform. The Brinell test will produce reliable results up to H_B values of around 400 and it is not recommended that the test be used on metals which would give values of H_B greater than 500. A comparison between H_B values and hardness values obtained from other tests is given in Table 2.4. H_B values and Vickers diamond hardness values, H_D, are comparable up to $H_B = 300$ but for higher hardness values there is a divergence between the two scales, with the H_B values being less than the H_D values for a given material.

Despite the shortcomings discussed above, the Brinell test is still widely used. When a 10 mm diameter indentor is used, the impression made is large in comparison to the crystal grain size of the metal and the hardness value obtained is representative of the mean hardness of the material. On the other hand, a large impression is often undesirable. Smaller sizes of indentor can be used in the Brinell test. Hardness testing machines designed to perform both Vickers diamond hardness and Brinell hardness measurements are usually supplied with 1 mm and 2 mm diameter ball indentors in addition to the diamond indentor used for the Vickers test. The recommended F/D^2 ratios (Table 2.2) should still be used, irrespective of the size of the ball indentor.

2.5 The Vickers Diamond Hardness Test

In the Vickers diamond test, the indentor used is a pyramidal shaped diamond and, as in the Brinell test, the indentor is forced into the surface of the material under the action of a static load for 10 to 15 seconds. As in the Brinell test, the Vickers Diamond hardness number, H_D, is given by

$$H_D = \frac{\text{Applied load (kg)}}{\text{Surface area of impression (mm}^2)}$$

The Vickers diamond hardness test is covered by BS 427(1961). The standard indentor is a square pyramid shape with an angle of 136° between opposite faces. One advantage of the Vickers test over the Brinell test is that the square impressions made are always geometrically similar, irrespective of size. The plastic flow patterns, therefore, are very similar for both deep and shallow indentations and, in consequence, the hardness value obtained is independent of the magnitude of the indenting force used.

After an impression has been made, the size of the impression is measured accurately using a microscope. Some hardness testing machines use an alternative system in which a magnified image of the impression is projected onto a screen and the size of this image measured, either with reference to a graticule inscribed on the screen or with a special rule. Both diagonals of the impression are measured and the mean value of D, the diagonal length, is used in the determination of the hardness number.

$$H_D = \frac{2F \sin \theta/2}{D^2}$$

where $\theta = 136°$, giving

$$H_D = \frac{1.8544F}{D^2}$$

where F is the applied load in kg, and D is the mean diagonal length in mm.

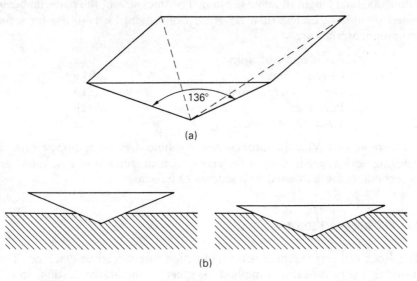

(a)

(b)

Figure 2.3 (a) Pyramid shaped diamond indentor, (b) Shallow and deep diamond impressions showing geometrical similarity.

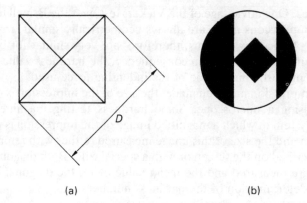

(a)   (b)

Figure 2.4 (a) Vickers diamond impression. The diagonal, D, is measured. (b) View through microscrope of Vickers machine. The micrometer shutters have been adjusted to the exact length of the impression diagonal.

The microscope of the standard Vickers hardness test machine has a pair of micrometer shutters built into the eyepiece. The shutters are adjusted until the impression is exactly bracketed between them (Figure 2.4(b)). The distance between the shutters is indicated on a digital counter attached to the eyepiece. The reading on this counter is termed the ocular reading and a set of tables is provided with the machine to convert the ocular reading into diamond hardness number, H_D, for a range of indenting loads. The ocular reading can be read to an accuracy of ± 0.001 mm. For the most accurate hardness results, the indenting load should be adjusted to give impressions with a diagonal length of about 0.5 mm. The thickness of the material being tested should not be less than $1.5 \times D$. Convenient loads to use for some common materials are

Steels and cast irons	30 kg
Copper alloys	10 kg
Pure copper, aluminium alloys	5 kg
Pure aluminium	2½ kg
Lead, tin, tin alloys	1 kg

The table of a Vickers hardness test machine may be equipped with an indexing device which enables the accurate measurement of case thickness in sectioned case-hardened components to be achieved.

2.6 The Rockwell Hardness Test

The Rockwell test machine is a rapid action direct-reading machine. This provides a very convenient method for speedy comparative testing. In this test, or rather series of tests, it is the depth of the impression which is measured and directly indicated by a pointer on a dial calibrated, inversely, into 100 division (1 scale division = 0.01 mm of impression depth). Consequently, a low scale number indicates a deep impression, hence a soft material, and vice versa. There are a series of Rockwell hardness scales because there are several indentors and several indenting loads available and covered by standards (BS 891(1962) refers to Rockwell hardness testing). The indentors used are hardened steel balls of various diameters or a diamond cone with an included angle of 120°. The standard ball indentors are of ¹⁄₁₆-inch (1.588 mm), ⅛-inch (3.175 mm), ¼-inch (6.350 mm) and ½-inch (12.70mm) diameter. The standard indenting loads are 60kg, 100 kg and 150 kg. Each separate scale of hardness is designated by a letter — A scale, B scale and so on. (Refer to Table 2.3.) A machine for performing Rockwell hardness tests is illustrated in Figure 2.5.

When an indentor is forced under load into a material, there is both elastic and plastic deformation but, because indentation hardness is the resistance to plastic deformation, the indenting load must be removed before the scale reading is taken. However, in order to ensure that a reliable scale reading is obtained, a small force should be applied to the indentor while a reading is being taken to make sure that the indentor is in full contact with the bottom of the impression. This is achieved in the Rockwell test by using a major load and a minor load. The use of these two loads is best illustrated by describing the sequence of operations involved in making a test.

(a) Bring the test sample into contact with the indentor and continue raising the sample against the indentor until a small inset pointer on the dial indicator has reached a reference setting mark. Doing this pushes the indentor up against a compression spring until the force exerted on the material by the spring, via the indentor, is equal to 10 kg.
(b) Set the main dial to the correct reference point (0 when using the diamond indentor, 30 when using a ball indentor).
(c) Apply the major load of 50 kg, 90 kg or 140 kg to give the required total load of 60 kg, 100 kg or 150 kg, according to the particular scale being used.
(d) Maintain the major load for between 4 and 7 seconds.
(e) Remove the major load to permit elastic recovery, while keeping the minor load on.
(f) Read off the hardness number from the dial.

The greatest reliability is achieved when the recorded hardness number lies between 20 and 70. A non-representative result is obtained if the sample being tested is too thin. The limiting thicknesses of materials for the various Rockwell scales are given in BS 891 (1962).

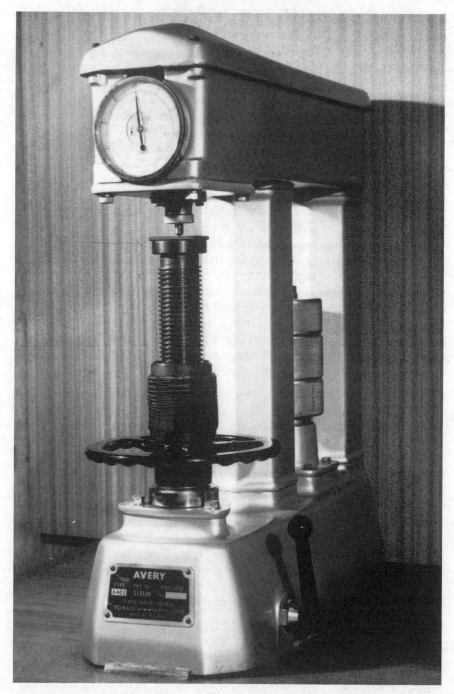

Figure 2.5 Rockwell direct reading hardness test machine.

The various Rockwell scales overlap and it is important that a correct choice of indentor and indenting load be made for the material being tested. The indentation depth must not exceed 100 scale divisions. It is also very important to note that when a Rockwell hardness number is quoted the actual Rockwell scale used must be indicated otherwise the result is meaningless. For example, H_{RB} refers to the B scale (namely a 100 kg total load, with a $\frac{1}{16}$-inch diameter ball indentor), while H_{RC} refers to the C scale (a 150 kg total load with a diamond cone indentor). The various scales and their applicability are given in Table 2.3.

Table 2.3 Rockwell hardness scales

Scale	Symbol	Indentor	Total Indenting Load (kg)	Material for which the scale is used
A	H_{RA}	Diamond cone	60	Thin hardened steel strip
B	H_{RB}	$\frac{1}{16}$-inch diameter steel ball	100	Mild steel and non-heat treated medium carbon steels
C	H_{RC}	Diamond cone	150	Hardened and tempered steels and alloy steels
D	H_{RD}	Diamond cone	100	Case hardened steels
E	H_{RE}	$\frac{1}{8}$-inch diameter steel ball	100	Cast iron, aluminium alloys and magnesium alloy
F	H_{RF}	$\frac{1}{16}$-inch diameter steel ball	60	Copper and brass
G	H_{RG}	$\frac{1}{16}$-inch diameter steel ball	150	Bronzes, gun metal and beryllium copper
H	H_{RH}	$\frac{1}{8}$-inch diameter steel ball	60	Soft aluminium and thermoplastics
K	H_{RK}	$\frac{1}{8}$-inch diameter steel ball	150	Aluminium and magnesium alloys
L	H_{RL}	$\frac{1}{4}$-inch diameter steel ball	60	Soft thermoplastics
M	H_{RM}	$\frac{1}{4}$-inch diameter steel ball	100	Thermoplastics
P	H_{RP}	$\frac{1}{4}$-inch diameter steel ball	150	Bearing materials and other very soft or thin materials
R	H_{RR}	$\frac{1}{2}$-inch diameter steel ball	60	Very soft thermoplastics
S	H_{RS}	$\frac{1}{2}$-inch diameter steel ball	100	Very soft or thin materials
V	H_{RV}	$\frac{1}{2}$-inch diameter steel ball	150	Very soft or thin materials

There are other Rockwell scales of hardness available. These scales, known as the N and T scales, are variants of the Rockwell A and B scales but involve smaller indenting forces and are suitable for hardness tests on thin samples. BS 4175(1961) is the relevant standard for these tests. The scales using the diamond cone indentor are known as the 15N, 30N and 45N scales and those using a $\frac{1}{16}$-inch diameter steel ball indentor are known as the 15T, 30T and 45T scales. In each case, the initial number refers to the total indenting force in kg. The method of conducting the N and T tests is exactly the same as for other Rockwell scales, with a pre-load of 10 kg applied before application of the major load.

2.7 Microhardness Testing

There are systems available for microhardness testing and the two most widely-used methods are the *Vickers Diamond* test and the *Knoop Diamond* test. The two methods are detailed in BS 5441 Part 6 and in the US ASTM Standard E 384–89. The principle of the Vickers Diamond microhardness test is basically the same as for the standard Vickers test but the indenting loads used are measured in grams rather than kilograms. This type of hardness testing is performed on a metallurgical microscope adapted for the purpose. The small pyramidal diamond indentor is embedded in the surface of a special objective lens. The surface of the test sample is prepared to a high polish and etched for micro-examination. When viewed under the microscope with a high magnification, usually some value between × 200 and × 2000, any particular micro-constituent or feature can be centred in the field of view and a micro-sized diamond indentation made using a small indenting load. The load used is usually of some value between 1 g and 100 g. The size of the square indentation is then carefully measured and the mean length of the diagonals, D, used to determine the hardness number, as given in Section 2.5. The accuracy of length measurement possible with a typical microscope attachment is of the order of ±0.0001 mm.

2.8 The Knoop Diamond Microhardness Test

The Knoop test was developed in the United States of America and utilises a diamond pyramid indentor designed to give a long thin impression, the length being seven times greater than the width and about thirty times greater than its depth (Figure. 2.6). This shape offers an advantage over the square pyramid of the Vickers test for microhardness work in that the length, l, of a Knoop impression is about three times greater than the

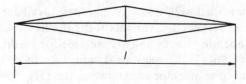

Figure 2.6 Shape of Knoop hardness impression.

diagonal, D, of a Vickers impression and can be measured with a greater degree of accuracy. The Knoop hardness number, H_K, is given by

$$\text{Hardness } H_K = \frac{\text{Load}}{\text{Projected area of impression}}$$

From the geometry of the indentor

$$H_K = \frac{10F}{l^2 \times 7.028}$$

The range of loads used with the Knoop indentor is similar to that used for Vickers microhardness tests. Knoop hardness test results are very similar to those obtained from the Vickers test but are consistently 20 or 25 numbers above Vickers values for the same material.

2.9 The Shore Scleroscope Test

This is a dynamic test and involves allowing a small diamond-tipped weight to fall freely through a known height onto the test-piece surface and measuring the height of rebound of the weight. In the test apparatus the small weight of a half ounce (14.2 g) falls freely through a height of 10 inches (250 mm) in a graduated glass tube onto the surface of the material being tested. The tube is graduated into 140 equal divisions. The rebound height of the weight is estimated, by eye, against the graduations on the tube. Several successive tests will be necessary to obtain a reliable reading but it is important that the scleroscope be moved to a different part of the surface for each test. This is because the impact of the weight causes some work hardening of the surface when it strikes. If a series of tests were made on the same spot on the surface, it would be noticed that the measured rebound height would increase in successive tests due to this work hardening effect. It is also important that the apparatus is set up with the glass tube vertical. In the US, scleroscope hardness testing is covered by ASTM Standard Practice E448–82. The standard Shore test equipment is equipped with a rubber bulb. One squeeze of the bulb will draw the weight to the top of the tube, where it is held by a retaining catch. A second squeeze of the bulb releases the catch, allowing the weight to fall freely. The Shore test is particularly useful for measuring the hardness of very hard metals and, because the test equipment is small and very portable, it is also very useful for the *in situ* testing of parts such as gears and the surfaces of the large rolls used in metal working operations. The relationships between Shore hardness values and the results of static indentation tests is given in Table 2.4.

As mentioned in Section 2.1, a dynamic test, such as the Shore test, can be used to gauge the elastic recovery response of a rubber-type material. While this is not the same as hardness, when the test is used for metals, the rebound values obtained with rubbers is termed their Shore hardness value and this parameter is a good indication of the quality of the rubber. The Shore value for rubber and plastic materials is generally determined using a small instrument known as a *durometer*, rather than using the standard Shore falling weight apparatus. A typical durometer is a compact hand-held device in which a round indentor is pressed into the material surface under the action of a spring or weight and a pointer registers a hardness value on a graduated scale. Various designs are available to cover the range of elastomers and plastics from the very soft to the very hard over the range Shore A to Shore D. The Barcol impressor is a similar type of instrument used for the determination of hardness of plastic materials. The hardness of rubbers and plastics is often quoted on the IHRD scale (International rubber hardness degrees). The IHRD scale closely approximates to the Shore scale.

2.10 Relationships between Hardness and Other Properties

As a general rule, it appears that for metals, as the hardness value increases, so also do properties such as tensile, compressive and shear strengths. There is no specific relationship between hardness and strength which holds for all metallic materials but some empirical equations have been used to estimate the tensile strengths of some metals from a hardness value. One such relationship, which is valid for annealed and normalised steels, is

$$\text{Tensile strength (MN/m}^2) = H_D \times 3.4$$

This equation does not hold for either heavily cold-worked steels or for austenitic steels. However, hardness testing, which is a rapid and relatively simple process, is used frequently as an approximate means for assessing the tensile strength of materials.

Similarly, there is a general trend between the hardness of metals and other properties, such as ductility and toughness. Most materials of high ductility tend to be relatively soft and the ductility decreases as the hardness of the material increases. Toughness, or its antithesis, brittleness also tends to vary with hardness with very hard materials having a tendency to be very brittle, but these are only tendencies and there are no empirical equations which enable a hardness number to be converted into, say, an impact strength value.

A work hardening index for a metal, the *Meyer index*, can be derived from a series of Brinell hardness tests. For this a series of hardness measurements are made using varying indenting loads but with the same sized ball indentor. The Meyer relationship is

$$F = a\, d^n$$

where F is the indenting load (kgf), d is the diameter of indentation (mm) and a and n are constants of the material and its condition. The resistance to indentor penetration is represented by a and n is the work hardening index.

The expression may be written

$$\ln F = \ln a + n \ln d$$

A graphical plot of $\ln F$ against $\ln d$ will give a straight line from which both a and n can be evaluated.

Table 2.4. Approximate hardness conversions

H_D	H_B	H_{RB}	H_{RC}	Shore	H_D	H_B	H_{RB}	H_{RC}	Shore
20	19				520	482		51.1	66.5
40	38				540	497		52.4	68.0
60	57				560	512		53.7	69.5
80	76	31.9			580	527		54.8	71.5
100	95	52.5			600	542		55.7	73.0
120	114	66.3			620	555		56.7	74.5
140	133	76.1			640	568		57.6	76.0
160	152	83.4			660	580		58.5	77.5
180	171	89.2			680	592		59.3	79.0
200	190	93.8	14.0	31.5	700	602		60.1	80.5
220	209	97.5	18.0	34.5	720			60.9	82.0
240	228		21.8	38.0	740			61.7	83.5
260	247		25.1	40.5	760			62.5	85.0
280	266		28.2	43.0	780			63.3	86.5
300	285		30.0	45.5	800			64.0	88.0
320	304		33.4	48.0	820			64.8	89.0
340	323		35.7	50.0	840			65.5	90.5
360	342		37.8	52.0	860			66.3	92.0
380	361		39.8	54.0	880			67.0	93.5
400	380		41.7	55.5	900			67.7	94.5
420	399		43.5	57.5	920				96.0
440	418		45.1	59.5	940				97.5
460	437		46.7	61.0	960				98.5
480	452		48.2	63.0	980				100.0
500	467		49.7	64.5	1000				101.0

2.11 Self Assessment Questions

2.1 Why is it necessary to use different loads when making Brinell hardness impressions on two different materials, say copper and a bronze?

2.2 What are the main advantages of the Vickers diamond test over the Brinell test?

2.3 (a) The mean diagonal length of a Vickers diamond impression made on a sample of aluminium using a 2.5 kg indenting load is 0.362 mm. What is the hardness of the aluminium?

(b) What size diamond impression would be made in the same material if an indenting load of 5 kg were used?

2.4 Why is it not correct to quote the hardness of a material as, say $H_R = 67$?

2.5 What is the main advantage of the Knoop hardness test over the Vickers microhardness test?

2.6 Repeated Shore tests on the same portion of a material's surface will give different hardness values. Why is this so?

2.7 Why are hardness tests used so frequently?

2.8 Brinell hardness impressions on a sample of annealed copper, using a 5 mm ball indenter, gave the following readings:

Load (kgf)	125	250	375
Indentation diameter (mm)	2.20	2.70	3.10

Determine whether these data obey the Meyer relationship and, if so, evaluate the Meyer constants.

3

Tensile, Compressive and Shear Tests

3.1 Stress and Strain

When a force is applied to a material, a stress will be developed within the material and this will generate a strain, which is a dimensional change. Strain may be elastic, meaning that the material will return to its original dimensions when the stress is removed, or it may be plastic or permanent, so that when the level of stress reduces to zero the material will not revert to its original dimensions.

When the strain is purely elastic, most materials conform to Hooke's law which states that the strain is directly proportional to the stress causing it.

Stress = strain × a constant

or Stress/strain = a constant

The constant is known as an elastic constant. There is more than one elastic constant, depending on the type of stress involved. A direct tensile force F acting on a body of length L will cause the body to extend by some amount x. The direct stress within the material caused by the force F is the force exerted per unit area. Stress has the units of newton/metre^2 (N/m^2). Strain is the dimensional change caused by stress and direct strain is the ratio of the change in length x to the original length L. (Figure 3.1). Strain, being a ratio, has no units. A shear force acting on a body causes a twisting effect (Figure 3.1 (c)).

A direct tensile or compressive stress will cause a direct strain and

$$\text{Direct stress/direct strain} = E$$

where E is the *modulus of elasticity* or *Young's modulus*.

Shear stress will produce a shear strain and the ratio

$$\text{Shear stress/shear strain} = G$$

where G is the *modulus of rigidity* or *shear modulus*. The elastic constants are fundamental properties of a material.

Plastic strain, unlike elastic strain is not directly proportional to stress. Metals and many plastic materials show both elastic and plastic behaviour, with deformation being wholly elastic at lower levels of stress but both elastic and plastic at higher stress values. The transition from elastic to plastic behaviour as the stress is increased may be gradual or sudden. In the latter case, the level of stress at which there is a sharp change to plastic deformation is termed the yield stress.

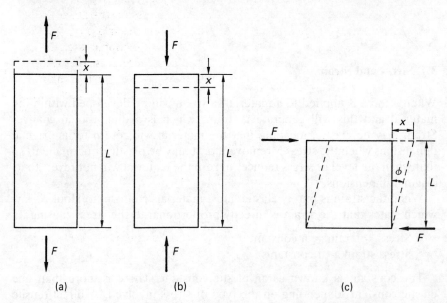

Figure 3.1 Elastic stress and strain: (a) tensile force F acting on body of length L and cross-sectional area A. Tensile stress $\sigma = F/A$. Tensile strain $\epsilon = x/L$; (b) compressive force F acting on body. Compressive stress $\sigma = F/A$. Compressive strain $\epsilon = -x/L$; (c) shear force F acting on body of cross-sectional area A. Shear stress $\tau = F/A$. Shear strain $\gamma = x/L = \tan \phi$.

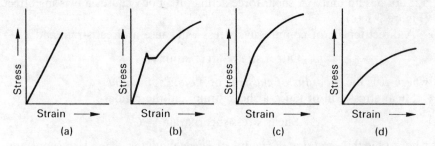

Figure 3.2 Types of nominal tensile stress/strain curve: (a) perfectly elastic to fracture point; (b) elastic and plastic strain with sudden yield; (c) elastic and plastic strain with no sharp yield; (d) no true elasticity.

Some materials do not deform plastically at all but are perfectly elastic at all values of stress up to the fracture point. Ceramics, glasses and a number of polymeric materials exhibit this type of behaviour. On the other hand, some materials, the soft thermoplastics, do not show true Hookean elasticity even at low levels of stress. The general types of stress/strain relationships are shown in Figure 3.2.

Generally, the data obtained during a tensile test are plotted as a force–extension curve and sometimes this type of curve is referred to, erroneously, as a stress–strain curve. The force–extension data obtained from a tensile test may be plotted in the form of stress and strain to give a nominal stress–nominal strain curve in which nominal stress, $\sigma_n = F/A_0$, where F is the force and A_0 is the original cross-sectional area of the test-piece, and nominal strain, $\epsilon_n = (L - L_0)/L_0$, where L is the extended length and L_0 is the original gauge length. Even so, such a nominal stress–strain curve is not a true stress–strain curve because it is based on the original test-piece dimensions and does not take into account the changes which occur during a test to destruction. A nominal stress–strain curve for a ductile metal, like a force–extension curve, shows a maximum before fracture. This is because, in a tensile test, there is a point of plastic instability, corresponding to the maximum on a force–extension or nominal stress–nominal strain curve, at which there is a sudden necking of the test-piece. If a true stress–true strain curve were drawn, this would show that stress increases steadily to fracture.

The true stress, $\sigma_t = F/A_i$, where A_i is the instantaneous cross-sectional area, and true strain,

$$\epsilon_t = \frac{dL}{L} = \ln\left(\frac{L}{L_0}\right) \text{ but } \frac{L}{L_0} = (1 + \epsilon_n)$$

so $\epsilon_t = \ln(1 + \epsilon_n)$ where L_0 is the initial gauge length and L is the instantaneous gauge length.

Assuming there is no volume change during plastic deformation, $A_i L = A_0 L_0$

$$\text{or } A_i = \frac{A_0 L_0}{L} \text{ so } \sigma_t = \frac{F L}{A_0 L_0} \text{ but } \frac{L}{L_0} = (1 + \epsilon_n). \text{ So}$$

$$\sigma_t = \frac{F}{A_0}(1 + \epsilon_n)$$

For most metals the relationship between true stress and true strain during plastic deformation can be written

$$\sigma_t = k \, \epsilon_t^n$$

where k and n are constants for the material. The constant n is the strain hardening exponent and the true stress–true strain equation is an empirical expression for work hardening. Instability and necking of a ductile metal occurs when $\epsilon_t = n$ and at this point, the maximum on the nominal stress–strain curve, the maximum value of σ_n, the nominal tensile strength of the material, is given by

$$\sigma_{max} = k\, n^n\, (1 - n)^{(1 - n)}$$

The tensile, compressive and shear properties of materials can be determined by testing. In the case of metals and many plastics materials, tensile testing is used to a much greater extent than compression or shear testing, mainly because the problems associated with this form of testing tend to be less. Materials such as concrete, ceramics and glasses are generally much stronger in compression than in tension (this is due mainly to the presence of porosity and other internal flaws) and tend to be used in situations where the service stresses are largely compressive. Compressive testing is widely used for this type of material. When it is required to know the tensile strength of such brittle materials, it is often determined by testing the material as a beam in bending using a three-point loading arrangement or by testing a cylindrical test-piece in diametral compression (see Section 3.6).

3.2 Testing Machines

There are many different types of testing machine available. Some are designed to perform one type of test, for example, tensile, while others are of the 'Universal' type and as such are suitable for uniaxial testing in both tension and compression and also for three-point bend tests on beam type test-pieces. Some designs are small 'table-top' machines with maximum force capacities ranging between 500 N and 20 kN, while at the other end of the scale large machines with load capacities of 1 MN or greater exist.

There are certain features which must exist in any testing machine be it for tensile, compressive or shear tests, and irrespective of size. These are

(a) a system for locating and holding the test-piece in a satisfactory manner,
(b) a mechanism for applying a force to the test-piece and for varying the force at a controlled rate,
(c) a system for accurate measurement of the applied force.

In addition, some designs of testing machines incorporate systems for the accurate measurement and recording of changes in test-piece dimensions but, generally, such measurements are made using separate devices, such as extensometers and torsionmeters, which can be attached to the test-piece.

The system used within a testing machine for the application of force may be either mechanical or hydraulic. The mechanical system normally comprises a screw, or screws, attached to the load-applying cross-head, and the screw is moved by means of a rotating nut. In hydraulic systems, the load is applied by a hydraulic ram moving in an oil-filled cylinder. In many test situations, it is important that the rate of strain is kept constant. Most types of machine have the facility for operating at several specific strain rates but some are capable of infinitely variable rates of strain between fixed upper and lower limits. The results obtained during the testing of metal samples is not affected by the rate of strain employed but polymeric materials are generally strain-rate sensitive. Specific rates of strain for these materials are recommended in the relevant standards.

The force applied to the test-piece may be measured in one of several ways. The oldest, but highly accurate, system is that involving a mechanical lever with a moveable jockey weight. The major disadvantage of the lever system is that it is bulky and occupies a lot of space, particularly for a large capacity machine. Some machine types, in which the load is applied hydraulically, use a hydraulic system for measuring the load on the test piece. In this arrangement, the increasing oil pressure, as the force is applied to the test-piece, moves a piston in a small calibrated pressure cylinder against a weighted pendulum lever, moving the pendulum out of the vertical position. As the force, and hence the oil pressure, increases so the pendulum is moved further from the vertical. Movement of the pendulum causes a pointer to move around the face of a calibrated dial scale. This is also a measurement system capable of high accuracy. Figure 3.3 shows a 40 kN Mohr and Federhaff hydraulic machine operating in the tensile mode. A

Figure 3.3 Mohr and Federhaff 40 kN hydraulic testing machine. The pendulum is visible and has been moved about 20° from the vertical by hydraulic pressure.

third system of load measurement utilises the deflection of a spring. This is the principle used in the small Monsanto Tensometer table-top machine in which the elastic deflection of a steel beam under load causes a piston to move in a small cylinder containing mercury. The mercury is forced into a glass tube mounted alongside a calibrated scale. A range of beams of varying degrees of stiffness is available to give a series of load ranges. A fourth system of load measurement involves the use of load cells. A load cell may be either a transducer, or a carefully prepared piece of material fitted with sensitive strain gauges. Application of a load creates an electrical output signal from the cell and this is amplified and presented as a digital meter read-out and/or a graphical display on a pen-recorder. The standards of accuracy for tensile testing machines are given in BS 1610.

3.3 Measurement of Strain

Many testing machines are fitted with autographic recorders which give a graphical display of the force–deflection behaviour of the test-piece. However, the graphs produced must be treated with caution. In a tensile test, for example, while an autographic record shows the correct shape of the force–extension diagram for the material and also shows accurate values of load applied, the readings on the extension axis refer to the separation distance between the test-piece holding grips and not the extension relative to the gauge length of the test sample. Some of the latest generation of testing machines are interfaced with a microcomputer and after completion of a test a full tabulated and graphical print-out of test results can be obtained including, if required, a comparison with previous test results.

The accurate measurement of test-piece dimensional change and, hence, strain is generally achieved by attaching a sensitive measurement device to the test-piece. The devices used for the measurement of longitudinal strain are termed extensometers and those designed to measure strain during a torsion test are termed torsionmeters.

One of the most commonly used extensometers is the Lindley type (Figure 3.4). This is a robust, yet sensitive, device. The Lindley extensometer is attached to a test-piece by tightening two screw grips, which are set 50 mm apart. When a force is applied to the test-piece and strain occurs, relative movement between the gripping points is transmitted through a lever to a dial gauge. The dial gauge is calibrated in steps equivalent to an extension of 0.001 mm and the maximum amount of extension which may be measured is 2.5 mm. Another type of extensometer using a mechanical principle is the Monsanto Hounsfield extensometer. In this instrument, a small relative movement between the gripping points causes a pair of electrical contacts to open. The contacts may be closed again, allowing a small bulb to light up, by turning a calibrated screw. Extensions of 0.01 mm can be read using this

Figure 3.4 Lindley extensometer positioned on a test-piece.

Figure 3.5 Monsanto Hounsfield type extensonmeter positioned on a tensile test-piece.

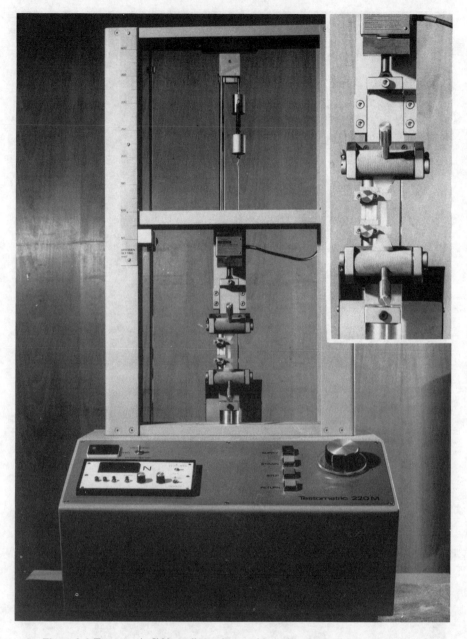

Figure 3.6 Testometric 5kN tensile testing machine with electronic extensometer.

instrument, but the applied force has to be held at a constant value while each extensometer reading is taken. This type of extensometer also operates on a gauge length of 50 mm (Figure 3.5).

Electronic extensometers are an integral feature of some of the newer generation testing machines, the extensions being displayed as a digital LED or LCD display. Such an arrangement is shown in Figure 3.6.

Some extensometers operate on an optical principle. One such is Marten's extensometer (Figure 3.7). A change in the gauge length of the material causes an angular movement of the mirror. A scale is viewed through the mirror by means of a telescope. Alternatively, a light source may project, by way of the mirror, a spot of light onto a graduated scale. Optical extensometers are highly sensitive and are often used for the measurement of small strains during long-term creep tests.

Another device which may be used for the measurement of strain is the electric resistance strain gauge. The resistivity of some conductors is very sensitive to variations in elastic strain. A resistance strain gauge consists of a zig-zag of very fine wire mounted between waterproof sheets. The gauge is securely bonded to the surface of the material under test and the ends of the wires connected to a bridge network so that changes in resistance can be measured. BS 3846 covers the calibration and grading of extensometers.

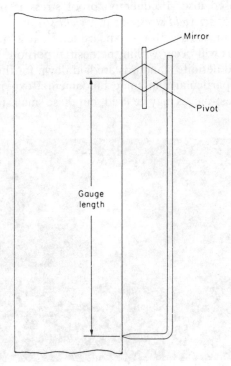

Figure 3.7 Principle of Marten's mirror extensometer.

In torsion testing a cylindrical shaped test-piece is subjected to axial torsion and the strain measurement which needs to be taken is the angle of twist. Figure 3.8 shows a torsionmeter with a 50 mm gauge length in position on a test-piece. The angle of twist can be read on the dial gauge to an accuracy of 0.001 radian.

3.4 The Tensile Testing of Metals

The results obtained in tensile testing are of considerable importance to engineers and designers. In many instances, a metal component does not have to fracture to be deemed to have failed in service; plastic deformation and buckling is failure and, in consequence, it is vital to know the level of stress at which plastic yielding begins. Some metals, principally steels, possess a pronounced *yield point*, but most show a smooth transition from elastic to plastic deformation behaviour. It may be difficult to determine the value of elastic limit with exactitude and the parameter proof stress is determined. This is the level of stress required to produce some specified small amount of plastic deformation. Often the amount of plastic strain specified is 0.1 per cent (nominal strain = 0.001) but other values of plastic strain may be used also. Frequently, proof stress is referred to by the alternative term *offset yield stress*, or just *yield stress*.

The metal test-pieces used for a standard tensile test are shaped in such a way that fractures will occur within the desired portion, that is, within the gauge length, and definite standards are laid down for their dimensions. In some instances, particularly in some fundamental experimental programmes, very small test-pieces may be used, but these small sizes are not quoted

Figure 3.8 Torsionmeter with 50 mm gauge length positioned on a torsion test-piece.

in the relevant testing standards as the results obtained from small test-pieces may not be truly representative of the properties of bulk material. The recommended dimensions for metal tensile test-pieces (Tables 3.1 and 3.2) are given in BS 18, Part 1: 1970, Parts 2, 3 and 4: 1971. (The testing of cast iron is covered in a separate publication, BS 1452: 1961).

It is important in a tensile test that the load be applied to the test-piece in a purely axial manner if fully representative results are to be obtained. The force is transmitted from the machine to the material through the test-piece holder. There are various types of test-piece holder available. The simplest system uses wedge grips (Figure 3.10). The wedge inserts have serrated surfaces to bite into the surface of the test-piece and hold it firmly. Wedge grips are manufactured to accept both flat and cylindrical test-pieces. One advantage of wedge grips is that no special preparation of test-piece ends is

Table 3.1 Round bar tensile test-pieces. Table of standard dimensions

S_0 (mm²)	d (mm)	L_0 (mm)	L_c (mm)	r wrought materials (mm)	r cast materials (mm)
200	15.96	80	88	15	30
150	13.82	69	76	13	26
100	11.28	50	62	10	20
50	7.98	40	44	8	16
25	5.64	28	31	5	10
12.5	3.99	20	21	4	8

d = Diameter of test-piece, L_0 = gauge length, L_c = parallel length, S_0 = original cross-sectional area, r = radius at shoulder (refer to Fig. 3.9(a)). For proportional test-pieces $L_0 = 5.65 \sqrt{S_0}$, $L_0 \simeq 5\,d$.

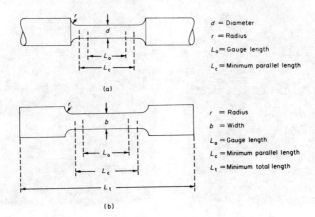

Figure 3.9 Types of tensile test piece: (a) round test-pieces; (b) flat test-pieces.

Table 3.2 Flat tensile test-pieces. Table of standard dimensions

b (mm)	L_0 (mm)	L_c (mm)	L_t (mm)	r (mm)
25	100	125	300	25
12.5	50	63	200	25
6	24	30	100	12
3	12	15	50	6

b = Width of test-piece, L_0 = gauge length, L_c = parallel length, L_t = total length, r = radius at shoulder (refer to Figure 3.9(b)).

Tables 3.1 and 3.2 are extracts from BS 18 and are reproduced by permission of the British Standards Institute, 2 Park Street, London W1A 2BS, from whom complete copies of the standard can be obtained.

(i)

(ii)

Figure 3.10 (a) Wedge grips: (i) for round bar and (ii) for sheet material.

needed but care must be taken when mounting flat specimens to ensure that correct alignment of the test-piece is achieved. Wedge grips are not suitable for holding very hard materials as the specimens may slip in the grips when a force is applied.

To overcome this latter problem, pin-type grips (Figure 3.11) are used for holding flat test-pieces, while round test-pieces are prepared with either screw-thread ends or shouldered ends and held as shown in Figure 3.12.

Figure 3.10 (b) Test-piece held in wedge grips.

Shouldered end test-pieces are not as widely used as the screw-thread end type because, for their preparation, they require larger diameter stock and a greater amount of material has to be removed by machining, making them very expensive to produce.

The shape of the load–extension curve for a non-ferrous metal is shown in Figure 3.13(a). The initial strain is elastic, but beyond point E, the elastic limit, strain is plastic. Point U is the maximum load, and this value of load is used for the determination of the tensile strength of the material. Point F marks the point of fracture. Although the applied load on the test-piece decreases beyond point U, the true stress acting on the test-piece, taking into account the reducing cross-sectional area, continues to increase until fracture occurs. (Refer to Section 3.1). In the commercial testing of metals, it is the load–extension curve, rather than a true stress–strain curve, that is plotted and strengths are calculated on the basis of the original cross-sectional area of a test-piece. The following information is determined in a routine tensile test.

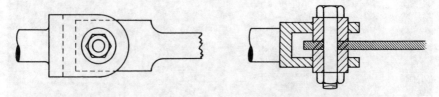

Figure 3.11 Pin-type grips for flat test-pieces.

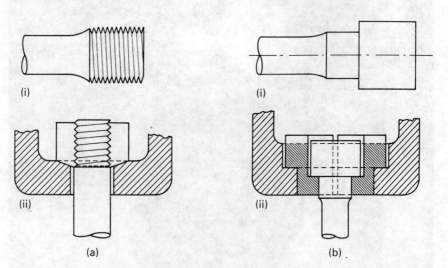

Figure 3.12 (a) (i) Screw-thread ended test-piece (ii) A holding arrangement for a screw-threaded test-piece, (b) (i) Shouldered test-piece end (ii) A holding arrangement for a shouldered test-piece.

1. *Tensile strength (T.S.)* (formerly known as ultimate tensile strength). This is based on the maximum load sustained by the test-piece, when the latter is tested to destruction, and corresponds to point U in Figure 3.13. The numerical value of tensile strength is calculated as a nominal stress and is given by

$$\text{T.S.} = \frac{\text{Maximum load applied}}{\text{Original cross-sectional area}}$$

The units in which tensile strength is normally quoted are megapascals (MPa), meganewtons per metre^2 (MN/m^2) or newtons per millimetre^2 (N/mm^2). Numerically these three values are equal. (In the construction industry, the units used generally are N/mm^2.)

2. *Yield point or yield stress.* There is a sharp discontinuity in the load–extension diagram for wrought iron and many steels (Figure 3.13 (b)) and the material will suddenly yield with little or no increase in the applied load necessary (point Y in the figure). The extent of this sudden yielding is about 5–7 per cent of the original gauge length. The yield point Y is close to, or coincident with, the elastic limit. The yield stress of the material is given by

$$\text{Yield stress} = \frac{\text{Applied load at the yield point}}{\text{Original cross-sectional area}}$$

3. *Limit of proportionality and elastic limit.* The limit of proportionality is the value of the stress at which the stress–strain curve ceases to be a straight line, i.e. the point at which Hooke's law ceases to apply. The elastic limit may be defined as the level of stress at which strain ceases to be wholly elastic. In most cases, these two values will be the same, but some polycrystalline metals do not completely obey Hooke's law. Such materials are termed anelastic, but the stress–strain curve does not vary greatly from linear. It is very difficult to determine a value for the limit of proportionality, as the values obtained depend on the sensitivities of the load-measuring system and the extensometer used. In general commercial testing the limit of proportionality is not usually reported. In its place, for metals which do not show a marked yield point, a *proof stress* is quoted.

4. *Proof stress or offset yield stress.* The proof stress for a material is the stress required to cause a specified permanent deformation, for example, 0.1 per cent, or 0.2 per cent of the original gauge length. (This may also be referred to as the 0.1 per cent or 0.2 per cent yield stress). In Figure 3.13(c) the load–extension diagram for some test-piece is shown in curve OEPUF. If OA corresponds to some percentage x of the original gauge length, and AP is drawn parallel to OE, then the point P denotes the x per cent proof load. The value for the x per cent proof stress is given by

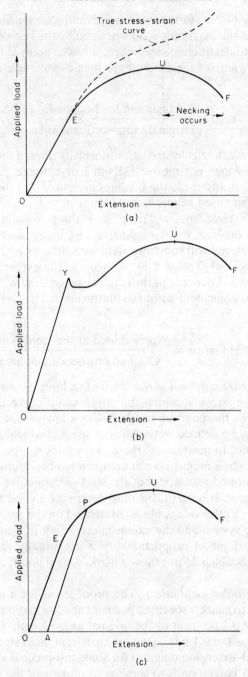

Figure 3.13 (a) Load–extension curve and its relation to a true stress–strain curve,
(b) Load–extension curve with sharp yield point (mild steel), (c) Determination
of proof load from load–extension diagram.

$$x \text{ per cent proof stress} = \frac{x \text{ per cent proof load}}{\text{Original cross-sectional area}}$$

In the United Kingdom, values are normally quoted for either the 0.1 per cent proof stress, or the 0.2 per cent proof stress, but in the USA it is customary to quote 0.2 per cent proof stress values. There will be a fairly wide difference between the value of proof stress and tensile strength for an annealed metal, but in a work-hardened metal, or in the case of a fairly hard and brittle material, the proof stress and tensile values will be fairly close to one another. The extent of the separation between proof stress and tensile strength values gives a measure of the amount of cold work that may be performed on the material.

5. *Modulus of elasticity, E, (Young's modulus).* The modulus of elasticity may be calculated from the slope of the straight line portion of the load-extension curve. E is given by (gauge length/cross-sectional area) × slope. The units in which E is quoted may be gigapascal (GPa), giganewton/metre² (GN/m²) or kilonewton/millimetre² (kN/mm²).

6. *Percentage elongation.* A definite length, the gauge length, is marked off on the test-piece before testing. After fracture, the two portions of the test-piece are placed together and the distance between gauge marks is remeasured. The amount of extension, expressed as a percentage of the original gauge length, is then quoted as the elongation value

$$\text{Percentage elongation on gauge length} = \left(\frac{L - L_0}{L_0}\right) \times 100$$

where L is the length between gauge marks after fracture and L_0 is the original gauge length. For an elongation figure to have any validity, the fracture must occur in the central section of the gauge length and the gauge length must be specified, for example, 'the percentage elongation on 50 mm is 20 per cent'. As the amount of plastic deformation of the test-piece is greatest nearest to the point of fracture, the elongation value for any particular material will be much higher if measured over a short gauge length than if measured over a long gauge length (see also the paragraph on the Barba's law below). The percentage elongation value for a material will give a measure of its ductility.

7. *Percentage reduction of area.* The percentage reduction of area is often quoted for round-bar specimens instead of a percentage elongation value. There is a certain merit in this as the reduction of area value is largely independent of specimen dimensions and gauge length. It is the difference in area between the cross-sectional area of the test-piece at the point of fracture and the original cross-sectional area, expressed as a percentage of the original cross-sectional area.

$$\text{Percentage reduction of area} = \left(\frac{A_0 - A}{A_0}\right) \times 100$$

where A_0 is the original cross-sectional area and A is the cross-sectional area at the point of fracture.

8. *Barba's law.* The plastic extension of a tensile test-piece is not uniform and is greatest in the necked region. The percentage elongation value, if taken on a short gauge length, will be greater than if taken over a long gauge length. Barba's law is an empirical equation relating the percentage elongation to gauge length and the cross-sectional area of test-pieces. The equation is

$$\text{Percentage elongation} = 100 \left(\frac{a\sqrt{A}}{L_0} + b \right)$$

where L_0 is the gauge length, A is the cross-sectional area and a and b are material constants.

3.5 The Tensile Testing of Plastics

The tensile testing of plastics materials is conducted in a generally similar way to the tensile testing of metals. There are differences, however, and these are necessary because of the different nature of plastics materials and metals. Many thermoplastic materials do not show Hookean elasticity even at low stress levels but are viscoelastic. In other words, the strain developed is not dependent on the level of stress alone, as would be the case for an elastic solid, but also depends on the length of time for which the stress is applied. One consequence of this is that variations in the rate of strain can give differences in the force–extension values and, hence different test results (Figure 3.14). It is recommended in the relevant standards publica-

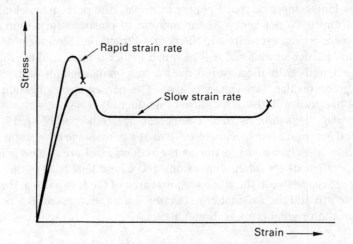

Figure 3.14 Influence of rate of strain on the force–extension values for a thermoplastic material.

tions that testing be conducted at comparatively high rates of strain (refer to BS 2782, Part 3, Methods 320A to 320F, 1976).

Unlike metals, many thermoplastic materials cold draw during a tensile test, and in these cases values are quoted for the yield stress and the drawing stress, these being

$$\text{Yield stress} = \frac{\text{Yield load}}{\text{Original c.s.a.}} \qquad \text{Draw stress} = \frac{\text{Drawing load}}{\text{Original c.s.a.}}$$

where c.s.a. is the cross-sectional area.

The phenomenon of cold drawing can occur in some thermoplastic materials and this is illustrated in Figure 3.15. At a stress corresponding to point Y in Figure 3.15(a), the test-piece necks down considerably and thereafter further strain takes place at a constant stress, usually slightly lower than the yield stress, with undrawn material being drawn into the necked zone. This drawn material is much stronger than the original undrawn plastic material due to the alignment of polymer molecules which occurs during drawing. The drawn state, with a more crystalline structure, is also referred to as stress induced crystallinity.

The load–extension curves that are obtained for many plastic materials either show no initial straight line portion, or show a departure from Hooke's law at very low values of applied load. In these cases, it would be very difficult, or impossible, to obtain a value for Young's modulus. The

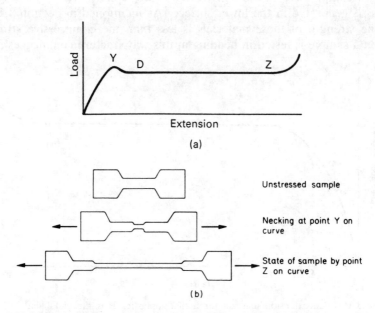

Figure 3.15 (a) Typical load-extension curve for a thermoplastic which cold draws. *Y* is yield load, *D* is draw load, (b) Stages in cold drawing of a test-piece.

value that is quoted as the modulus of elasticity, E, for plastics is in fact a *secant modulus*, and is obtained by determining the stress at a value of 0.2 per cent strain (see Figure 3.16).

Many thermoplastics extend to a very considerable extent during a tensile test, but there is an almost instantaneous recovery of much of this strain as soon as the test-piece fractures. The elongation value quoted for thermoplastics is known as the *percentage elongation at break*, and is determined by noting the distance between the gauge marks at the moment of fracture, and not by placing the fractured portions together after the test, as is the case with tests on metals.

3.6 Determining the Tensile Strength of Brittle Materials

The axial tensile testing of brittle materials, such as ceramics and glasses, would be extremely difficult, if not impossible, because of the problems of preparing suitable shaped test-pieces and those of effectively holding them within the testing machine. It is customary to determine the fracture strength from a three-point bend test. Flexural bend tests are used also for testing concretes and reinforced plastics materials. The flexural strength value determined in this type of test is also known as the *modulus of rupture* of the material. When a sample is subjected to bending, as shown in Figure 3.17, a compressive stress is generated in the upper surface and a tensile stress is generated in the lower surface. As mentioned in Section 3.1, the tensile strength of these materials is less than the compressive strength. When a sample is tested in bending in this way fracture commences at the

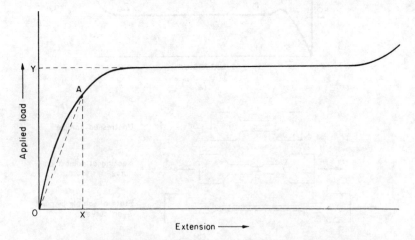

Figure 3.16 Load–extension diagram for a thermoplastic. Y is the yield load. OX is an extension corresponding to a strain of 0.2%. The slope of the straight line OA is used to determine the modulus of elasticity for the plastic, the secant modulus.

tensile surface so the breaking load, F, is related to the tensile strength of the material. The magnitude of the direct stress, σ is related to the bending moment, M, by the general bending equation:

$$\frac{\sigma}{y} = \frac{M}{I}$$

where y is the distance from the neutral surface (half the thickness for a sample of symmetrical section) and I is the second moment of area of the section.

$I = \dfrac{BD^3}{12}$ for a rectangular section of width B and thickness D

$I = \dfrac{\pi D^4}{64}$ for a circular section of diameter D

The maximum value of bending moment for a symmetrical three-point loading system as in Figure 3.16 is $FL/4$ and so

$$\sigma = \frac{My}{I} = \frac{FLD}{8I}$$

For a sample of rectangular section, therefore

$$\sigma = \frac{3FL}{2BD^2}$$

The modulus of rupture value for a material is approximately double the true tensile strength. This mode of testing is also used to determine the fracture strength of rigid thermoset materials including laminated plastics such as 'Tufnol', a phenol-formaldehyde resin laminated with either cloth or paper, and is covered by BS 2782, Part 3, Method 3554,1970. Figure 3.18 shows a three-point loading attachment for a Monsanto Hounsfield testing machine.

Another indirect method which may be used to determine a tensile strength is the split cylinder test. This type of test, shown diagrammatically

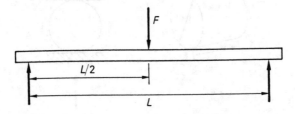

Figure 3.17 Three-point loading arrangement.

in Figure 3.19, is widely used for determining the tensile strength of concrete and is detailed in BS 1881; Part 117, 1983. As the compression force is imposed, circumferential tensile stresses are induced in the material, these having maximum value at the central horizontal plane. The cylinder will eventually fail and split at this plane. The value of the tensile stress, σ, at

Figure 3.18 Three-point loading attachment with Tufnol test-piece in position, on a Monsanto Hounsfield testing machine.

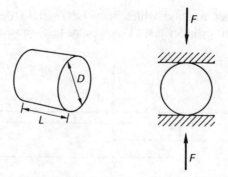

Figure 3.19 Principle of split cylinder test for assessing the tensile strength of concrete.

failure is given by

$$\sigma = \frac{2F}{\pi LD}$$

where F is the maximum force applied, L is the cylinder length and D is its diameter.

3.7 Compression Testing

The compression testing of metals is little used. A tensile test sample is fairly long and waisted down to give a parallel-sided central portion, within which the tensile characteristics of the material can be accurately assessed. In compression testing, a long sample cannot be used because buckling failure would occur rather than direct axial compression. Test-pieces have to be short and the length not be greater than three times the diameter to avoid buckling. The other problem is that of friction between the ends of the test-piece and the platens of the testing machine. As compressive strain occurs, reducing the test-piece length, so there is a corresponding increase in the diameter of the sample. Friction hinders lateral expansion of the diameter at the test-piece ends and once plastic deformation occurs the material tends to deform into a barrel shape, as shown in Figure 3.20. This type of deformation generates tensile stresses at the surface of the material and failure is based more on the tensile strength of the material than anything else. Brittle materials, when tested in compression, normally fail by shear at 45° to the direct stress axis. The type of fracture may be either of the double cone type or straight shear (Figure 3.21). These failure modes apply to all brittle materials, whether metallic or non-metallic.

Figure 3.20 Plastic deformation of a ductile compression test-piece.

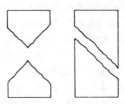

Figure 3.21 Failure modes of a brittle compression test-piece: (a) double cone type failure; (b) shear type failure.

Compressive test-pieces tend to be small and of cylindrical shape, as mentioned above, but compression test samples of cement or concrete are often cast into cube shapes, with edge lengths of either 100 or 150 mm (see BS 1881, Part 116, 1983), or cylinders (see ASTM Standards C39–86 and C873–85).

3.8 Testing in Shear

There are two main types of test which may be used for the determination of the properties of a material in shear. One is based on the application of a torque to a cylindrical sample, causing the test-piece to twist, while the other involves direct shear. There are problems associated with both types of test. The former method causes the development of an almost pure shear stress within the material, but the shear stress is not uniform throughout and varies from zero at the central axis to a maximum value at the surface of the cylinder. For pure torsion on a cylinder, the general torsion equation applies within the elastic range.

$$\frac{\tau}{r} = \frac{T}{J} = \frac{G\theta}{L}$$

where τ is the shear stress at radius r from the central axis, T is the applied torque, J is the second polar moment of area, G is the modulus of rigidity of the material, and θ is the angle of twist in radians over the gauge length, L, of the test-piece.

The value of J for a solid cylindrical section is given by $\pi D^4/32$ and for a hollow cylindrical section by $\pi(D^4 - d^4)/32$ where D and d are the outside and inside diameters, respectively.

As the applied torque, T, is increased so the angle of twist, θ, increases in direct proportion within the elastic range. The fact that the level of shear stress varies across a diameter is relatively unimportant when all stresses and strains are elastic. However, where the surface shear stress reaches the elastic limit and plastic strain commences, results become unreliable. Plastic deformation tends to spread inwards in an irregular manner. Materials, such as mild steel, with a pronounced yield point tend to show greater irregularities than other metals. One method used to reduce the problems is to employ hollow cylindrical test-pieces. In this way, differences between the value of shear stress at outer and inner surfaces and reduced, but a further problem is encountered. The tendency for plastic buckling of the tubular specimen increases rapidly as the wall thickness is reduced.

There is no British Standard for torsion testing but the ASTM Standard E143–81 covers the determination of shear modulus.

The results of a torsion test may be plotted graphically in the form torque, T, against angle of twist, θ. The value of the modulus of rigidity, G, may be obtained from the slope of the linear elastic portion of the curve (T/θ).

Direct shear tests are sometimes used but it is very difficult to obtain accurate quantitative data from them. Several systems have been adopted and they are illustrated in Figure 3.22. The test equipment generally takes the form of attachments which can be used in conjunction with a universal testing machine. Round bar samples may be tested in double shear using a fork and eye device, as shown in Figure 3.22(a). Hardened steel bushes of various sizes will accommodate bars of differing diameter. Figure 3.22(b) shows the principle of the double knife shear system which can be used in conjunction with bar samples of rectangular section. A third type of test, suitable for sheet material takes the form of a punch and die to shear a disc from the sheet.

These three methods all suffer from the same disadvantage. Even when all parts of the attachments are made to close dimensional tolerances from very hard materials, there will be some bending of the test-piece and the stresses within the material will not be of the pure shear type but will include bending stresses. The results of such tests, while not providing fundamental values of shear strength, can be used to give a qualitative assessment and indicate the behaviour patterns of the material for fabrication processes involving blanking and shearing.

3.9 Significance of Test Results

Of the various tests described in the foregoing paragraphs, it is the tensile test which is the most widely used for metals and plastics materials. This is

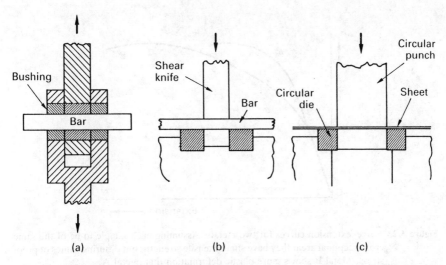

Figure 3.22 Methods of direct shear testing; (a) principle of 'fork and eye' method for double shear of round bars; (b) principle of double knife shear method for flat bars; (c) principle of disc shear of sheet material by punch and die.

because consistent test results can be achieved in this type of test. If a large number of tests were carried out on samples from the same batch of material the extent of deviation from mean values would be of a small order, provided that the test-pieces were correctly prepared and that they were properly held in suitable grips so that forces were purely axial.

For the designer and end user of the material, a knowledge of the strength of the material is of the utmost importance. Although tensile strength seems to be the most quoted property for metals and plastics, it is the yield or proof stress value which is of greater importance as this is the level of stress at which the material will begin to deform irreversibly. In the design of structural components, a designer will use strength values of materials when calculating the dimensions necessary to accommodate the predicted service stresses but will incorporate a factor of safety. In many codes of practice, this factor is based on the yield or proof stress value but in others it is based on the value of tensile strength.

The ductility of a material is of major importance to the manufacturer. Sheet material, which may be used to form a wide range of shapes from saucepans and kettles to car body shells, needs to possess good ductility. The value of percentage elongation is a good guide to this property but a better assessment can be obtained by examining the difference between yield or proof stress and the tensile strength. Figure 3.23 shows tensile force–extension curves for two metal samples. The metals have similar tensile strengths but the proof stress of material B is lower that that of material A. It can be seen from the general form of the curves that metal B has a greater capacity for plastic deformation than metal A. The area under

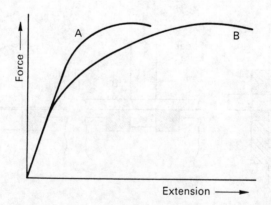

Figure 3.23 Force–extension curves for two metals. Assuming each sample to be of the same cross-sectional area, they have similar tensile strengths but differing values of proof stress. Metal B shows more plastic deformation than metal A.

the plastic portions of the curves is an indication of the amount of plastic deformation which can be performed.

The tensile properties of brittle materials are not as consistent as those of ductile metals. This is because of the presence of micro-cracks and other small defects which are always found in these materials. One test result only may not be representative of the material, and a series of tests on a number of samples from the same batch of material may show a wide deviation from the mean value. The three-point load flexure test to determine the tensile strength (modulus of rupture) is a reliable test, provided a sufficient number of samples are taken.

The compression test is rarely used to determine the properties of metals and polymers but is widely used for ceramics and particularly for cements and concretes. The compressive strengths of these materials are considerably greater than their tensile strengths and so they tend to be used to a large extent in situations where the major stresses are compressive. The micro-cracks and other defects which cause major variations in tensile strength values do not greatly influence the compressive strength and, thus, the results of compression tests on concretes and ceramics tend to be reliable.

As stated in Section 3.8, there are certain problems associated with shear tests. Torsion tests can give reliable assessments of the shear properties of a material within the elastic range and can also give information on the plasticity of a material, but a complete analysis of results is difficult because of the presence of stress gradients in torsion. It is also difficult to analyse the results of the direct shear type of test because there will always be some bending occurring in such tests. These direct shear tests tend to simulate some of the operations used in the fabrication of metal components but the results of such tests tend to be qualitative rather than quantitative.

3.10 Self Assessment Questions

3.1 List the main parameters which may be determined in a full tensile test.

3.2 One of the results of a tensile test is quoted as: Percentage elongation = 17%. Is there anything wrong in expressing the result in this manner?

3.3 List the main differences between the standard tensile test for metals and that for plastics.

3.4 The data recorded during a tensile test on a material are given in Table 3.3. Test piece dimensions: width = 12.61 mm, thickness = 3.47 mm, gauge length = 50 mm. Force recorded at break = 1290 N. Length between gauge marks at break = 97 mm. Evaluate the tensile properties of the material. What type of material was tested?

3.5 How can the tensile strength of a ceramic or glass be determined?

Table 3.3

Force (N)	Extension (mm)
25	0.018
50	0.040
75	0.064
100	0.090
125	0.121
150	0.153
175	0.192
200	0.238
225	0.293
250	0.355
275	0.425
300	0.520

3.6 A concrete cylinder of 100 mm diameter and 100 mm length is subjected to a diametral compressive force. The value of force at failure point is 47.5 kN. What is the tensile strength of the concrete?

3.7 What are the main reasons for making direct shear tests?

3.8 Why is compression testing used more for ceramics and concretes than for metals?

4

Sheet Metal Tests

4.1 Introduction

A wide variety of products is made from sheet metal using processes such as bending and folding, pressing, deep drawing and spinning. All these processes involve subjecting the material to considerable plastic deformation and the sheet metal must possess sufficient ductility for it to perform well during the forming process. The value of percentage elongation determined in a standard tensile test gives a reasonable indication of ductility but it may not be sufficiently sensitive to indicate the ability of the material to be shaped satisfactorily into a finished article by one of the sheet metal forming processes.

A number of special tests have been developed as a means of assessing the formability of sheet metal and a few of these are considered in this chapter. Free bend, controlled bend, and reverse bend tests are covered in BS 1639(1964).

4.2 Controlled Bend Tests

A controlled bend test is one in which the material is caused to bend around a former of some specific radius. A commonly used test of this type involves bending the sheet through 180°. The main reasons for using such a test are to assess the ductility of the material and to determine the minimum bending radius possible for the material without fracture occurring.

A series of formers, with varying edge radii, are used and samples of sheet metal are bent around the formers. To ensure that the material bends closely around the former, the sheet metal is forced into a soft rubber block. (Figure 4.1) The bending may be carried out either by using a universal testing machine in the compression mode or using a purpose-built bend test machine. Tests are conducted with several formers to determine the smallest bend radius that the sheet material can be formed around with no incidence of cracking.

The limiting bend radius is a function of the thickness of the material as well as metallurgical quality and so the results of the bend test are expressed in terms of sheet thickness, as follows: 1T, 2T, 3T etc. A limiting bend radius of 2T for a sample of sheet of 1.5 mm thickness would mean that the smallest radius for a 180° bend without cracking would be twice the sheet thickness, namely 3 mm. Very ductile materials which show no signs of cracking after bending around the smallest radius former may be taken a stage further by having the sides flattened against each other after removal from the former. The bend test result is recorded as FLAT if there are still no signs of cracking after this severe deformation. This type of controlled bend test can be used for wire as well as for sheet material.

Controlled bend tests are not always performed by bending through a full 180°. The suitability of a material for a particular type of forming process might be best served by bending through some smaller angle and assessing the results. A further application of a controlled bend test is to determine the elastic 'spring back' of a material. In order to produce a component with a final bend angle of, say 90°, the material would have to be formed through some angle greater than 90° so that there is a set angle of 90° after the deforming force is removed and elastic recovery has occurred. The amount of elastic recovery for a given material can be measured using a controlled bend test.

4.3 Reverse Bend Tests

Reverse bend tests yield results of a purely empirical character. The tests are used to give some guide both to the amount of plastic deformation which may be given to a material and the rate at which the material work hardens.

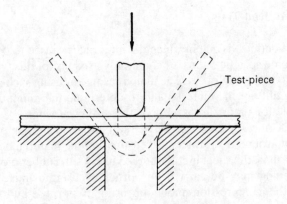

Test-piece

Figure 4.1 Making a controlled bend test.

In one such test, a strip of the material is clamped in a vice with rounded jaws and is then bent, firstly through 90° (to position A in Figure 4.2) then through 180° to position B in Figure 4.2 and thereafter backwards and forwards between these positions until a crack appears. The number of bends to fracture is noted, the first bend through 90° being counted as a half-bend. Test-pieces, cut from sheet material, are generally 50 mm by 12.5 mm in size and the test is suitable for material of up to 2 mm in thickness. The radius at the jaws should be 1 mm for all sheet thicknesses up to 0.4 mm. For greater test-piece thickness, jaw radii of 2 mm, 3 mm or 6 mm are used. For any given material, the change in the radius of the jaws will affect the number of reversals to failure considerably. For example, with sheet samples of 0.5 mm thickness, the number of bends to failure when bent over a jaw radius of 2 mm may be two to three times greater than when tested over a 1 mm jaw radius.

This type of bend test is also used in connection with wire. Another type of reverse bend test used for wires is the wire wrapping test. In this test, the wire is gripped in a vice and then one portion of the wire is close wrapped around the other, as shown in Figure 4.3.

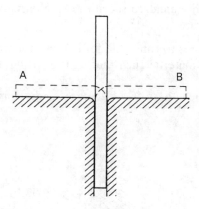

Figure 4.2 Principle of reverse bend test.

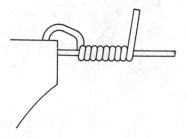

Figure 4.3 Wire wrapping test.

The wire is wrapped six times around its own diameter in one direction, unwrapped, straightened and then wrapped six times around its own diameter in the same direction as at first. The wire should remain unbroken to pass the test. In some cases a specification may only call for one wrapping to be conducted.

4.4 The Erichsen Test

There are a number of tests which may be used to give a guide to the suitability of sheet material for cold forming. In the USA these are referred to as ball punch deformation tests. One test procedure in general use is the Erichsen test and this mainly assesses ductility and stretch formability.

The principle of the Erichsen test is that a sheet metal test-piece, circular or square, is held in position over a circular die of 27 mm diameter and an indenting head, with a nose diameter of 10 mm, is forced into the surface of the sheet (Figure 4.4). The distance moved by the indenting head is read from a scale calibrated in divisions of 0.1 mm and the *Erichsen Number* is the depth in mm moved by the indentor to the end point. The test is covered by BS 3855(1965) and this standard specifies two alternative end points which may be used. These are

(a) indentor movement to cause the formation of a crack through the full thickness of the material such that light is visible through part of the crack length or

(b) the point at which there is a decrease in the force sustained by the test-piece.

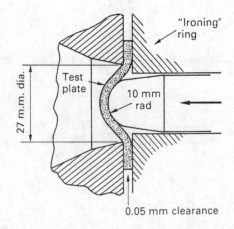

Figure 4.4 Principle of Erichsen cupping test.

It is important to note that when an Erichsen number is quoted the end point criterion used MUST be stated otherwise the number has no value. The test is suitable for sheet material in thicknesses ranging from 0.1 mm to 2 mm. The minimum size of test-piece is 80 mm in diameter or 80 mm square.

The results of an Erichsen test are quantitative, in terms of the depth of penetration to an end point, but qualitative information can also be obtained from interpretation of the appearance of the cup produced. The surface of the dome produced in the test may have a smooth texture or it may show a rough, uneven, texture — the *orange peel* effect. This latter is evidence of a coarse grain structure in the material rendering it unsuitable for drawing and pressing operations. The type of crack formed is also an important guide. For good formability, the fracture should be circumferential, indicating isotropic properties in the sheet. The formation of tangential crack denotes directionality in the sheet, while a central crack across the top of the dome can occur both in materials of low ductility and in those showing directionality.

4.5 The Jovignot Cupping Test

In the Jovignot test, a circular sheet metal test-piece is securely clamped over the end of a hydraulic cylinder and the pressure slowly increased. Plastic deformation of the sheet occurs and a form, approximately spherical, is generated. The pressure is increased until the test-piece fractures and the extent of the deformation is noted.

The stress at fracture can be calculated by

$$\text{Stress} = \frac{P R}{2 t}$$

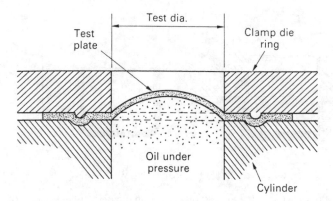

Figure 4.5 Jovignot test.

where P is the pressure, t is the sheet thickness and R is the radius of curvature of the deformed sheet. The radius of curvature can be calculated using the theorem of intersecting chords

$$r^2 = h(2R - h)$$

Therefore

$$R = \frac{r^2 + h^2}{2h}$$

where r is the forming area radius and h is the inside depth of cup.

A measure of the ductility of the sheet metal is given by the *cupping coefficient*. This is based on the increase in surface area during the test. The cupping coefficient is given as the ratio h^2/r^2

4.6 Cup Drawing Tests

The tests described in Sections 4.4 and 4.5 provide information about ductility and preferred orientation, or directionality, within the sheet material but they do not give an assessment of the material's ability to be deep drawn successfully. A cup drawing test, which involves the production of a cylindrical cup from a circle of sheet material by means of a deep drawing process, is the only reliable means for giving an assessment of this aspect of formability.

A true deep drawing operation is one in which the sheet material is drawn through the annular space between a punch and die with the clearance between punch and die being less than the thickness of the sheet material. The arrangement for a cup draw test is shown in Figure 4.6. The circular

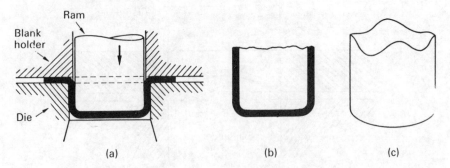

Figure 4.6 Principle of a cup draw test: (a) drawing in progress; (b) drawn cup; (c) earred cup produced from sheet showing directionality.

blank is held in position by a clamp. Sufficient pressure is exerted by the clamp to prevent the sheet from wrinkling as it is drawn into the die, but the clamping pressure must not be too great otherwise movement of the sheet into the die would be hindered and the material would tear, rather than be drawn. A series of punches of differing diameters should be available so as to provide various punch/die clearances to accommodate sheet samples of different thicknesses.

There is no standard cup draw test and deep draw punch and die sets of several sizes have been produced to give cylindrical drawn cups of 25 mm, 50 mm or 75 mm diameter with either flat or rounded bases.

In order to be drawn successfully, a material should be of good ductility, possess a fine and uniform crystal grain size with little, if any, directionality of properties remaining after the rolling and annealing processes. Sheet metal with insufficient ductility will tear during the drawing operation. Directionality in the material may cause it to tear during the draw but, even if tearing does not occur, the drawn cup will possess ears (Figure 4.6(c)). The formation of ears of small size during the manufacture of deep drawn articles may be tolerated as the ears can be trimmed from the drawn article without the loss of a great deal of material. However, severe directionality, leading to the formation of large ears, would render the material unsuitable for use in deep drawing operations.

4.7 Self Assessment Questions

4.1 What are the main reasons for carrying out bend tests, and what types of material are these tests used for?

4.2 The result of a controlled bend test on mild steel sheet of 1.3 mm diameter is quoted as 1T. What does this signify?

4.3 Describe the principle of the Erichsen test.

4.4 What information can be obtained from the Erichsen test?

4.5 What is meant by the term cupping coefficient in the Jovignot test?

4.6 For what purposes are cup draw tests used?

4.7 What are 'ears' and why are they formed?

5

Notch Impact and Fracture Toughness Testing

5.1 Fracture

When an external stress is applied to a material, the material will be deformed, or strained. If the magnitude of the stress is increased, the material will eventually fail by fracturing. Not all materials fail in the same manner, and the type of fracture that occurs may be either brittle or ductile. In a ductile fracture, failure is preceded by a considerable amount of plastic deformation of the material, but in a brittle, or non-ductile, fracture there is little or no plastic deformation prior to failure. The type of failure that occurs is largely dependent on the nature of the material and its condition, but failure is also affected by other factors, including the type of stressing, the rate of application of stress, temperature, and environment.

Brittle fracture

Brittle failure is best explained in terms of the Griffith crack theory. According to this theory, very small cracks are normally present within the material and the stress, σ_c, necessary to cause a crack to propagate is given by the expression

$$\sigma_c = \left[\frac{2 \gamma E}{\pi c} \right]^{1/2} \text{(plane stress condition)}$$

$$\sigma_c = \left[\frac{2 \gamma E}{\pi(1 - v^2) c} \right]^{1/2} \text{(plane strain condition)}$$

where γ is the surface energy per unit area, E is Young's modulus for the material, c is one-half of the crack length, normal to the axis of stress, and v is Poisson's ratio.

Once the applied stress has reached the level σ_c, small internal cracks can propagate, but as the cracks increase in size and the value of c increases, so σ_c decreases and the cracks spread catastrophically. The rate at which such a crack propagates in a brittle material is about the speed of sound. This failure mode applies to all brittle solids.

In many materials, there is some plastic deformation at a crack tip prior to crack extension and fracture. The Griffith relationships were modified by Orowan and Irwin to take account of this. In the modified equations the term $2\gamma E$ is replaced by $G_c E$, where G_c is the energy required to produce a unit area of crack, has the units J/m^2, and is a constant for the material. G_c is referred to as the *toughness* of the material.

Fast fracture

Fast fracture, a catastrophic failure, can occur in metals containing small cracks or flaws, which in other circumstances would be expected to plastically deform or yield. Fast fracture is the growth at around the speed of sound of cracks within the material which suddenly become unstable. The modified Griffith equation $\sigma = (G_c E/\pi c)^{1/2}$ can be written as

$$\sigma(\pi c)^{1/2} = (G_c E)^{1/2}$$

The symbol K may be used in place of the term $\sigma(\pi c)^{1/2}$ and K is known as the *stress intensity factor*. Fast fracture will occur when K reaches a value of K_c, that is a critical combination of crack dimension and stress. K_c, which is equal to $(G_c E)^{1/2}$, is the *critical stress intensity*, or *fracture toughness* of the material and is a very important constant of a material. It has the units MPa $m^{1/2}$ (MN $m^{-3/2}$). The critical stress for fast fracture, σ_c, is given then by

$$\sigma_c = \frac{K_c}{(\pi c)^{1/2}}$$

where c is one-half of the crack length. When c is small σ_c will be greater than σ_y, the yield strength of the metal, but when the crack reaches a critical size the value of σ_f will be equal to σ_y and fast fracture will occur with no plastic yielding.

The rate of application of stress has an effect on the amount of plastic deformation and the type of fracture obtained. Plastic flow is, to some extent, time dependent. There is an internal frictional resistance to the movement of dislocations within metals, and time is required in order to allow dislocations to overcome this resistance, and to pass potential barriers, such as impurity and solute atoms and grain boundaries. When the rate of application of stress is low, plastic deformation occurs normally, but as the rate of stress increase approaches the limiting rate of slip, the stress level necessary to move dislocations begins to increase. In other words, a high rate of loading will increase the yield strength of a metal. (There is a similar effect in thermoplastic materials, although the mechanism of plastic deformation differs from that in metals). If the rate of stressing is very high, as in conditions of impact loading, failure may occur without prior plastic deformation (brittle failure). Face-centred cubic metals, possessing many regular slip planes, are not very sensitive to changes in strain rate and do not show brittle failure even under conditions of impact loading. Metals that crystallise in the body-centred cubic or in the close-packed hexagonal forms are, however, sensitive to changes in strain rate and may fail in a wholly brittle manner under conditions of impact loading.

Other factors that have an effect on the failure behaviour of a material are component geometry and surface condition. A sudden change of section, or a surface notch, will act as a point of stress concentration within the material. The stress concentration factor increases as the fillet radius at a sectional change is reduced, or as the root radius of a notch is reduced. Such points of high stress concentration will greatly increase the possibility of brittle failure under impact loading conditions, although not all materials possess the same degree of notch sensitivity. Materials that are generally brittle are usually highly sensitive to the presence of notches and sharp sectional changes. Ductile metals, on the other hand, possess low notch sensitivities because plastic flow can take place in the neighbourhood of a point of high stress concentration with the effect of increasing the root radius of a notch, and consequently causing a reduction of the stress-concentration effect. Inclusions, angular-shaped constituent particles, and porosity can also act as points of stress concentration within a material, and their presence will increase the possibility of brittle failure.

5.2 Temperature Effects and the Ductile–brittle Transition

A change in temperature will affect the behaviour of a material. In metals, any increase in temperature will render dislocations more mobile and hence will cause a reduction in the yield strength. Conversely, a decrease in temperature will be reflected in an increased yield strength. Face-centred cubic metals are ductile at all temperatures, but metals that are body-centred cubic or hexagonal in structure undergo a change from brittle to ductile behaviour as the temperature is raised. For example, zinc is brittle at ordinary temperatures, but will deform plastically at temperatures in excess of 100°C. Low carbon steels are ductile at low strain rates at all temperatures above a value of about $-170°C$, but when they are subjected to impact loading conditions there is a transition from a tough fibrous fracture to a brittle cleavage fracture over a narrow range of temperature close to 0°C. The energy absorbed in fracturing a notched mild steel test-piece in a Charpy impact test may reduce from about 1600 kJ/m^2 at +15 °C to about 150 kJ/m^2 at $-5°C$. Tough and brittle fractures are shown in Figure 5.2.

The cleavage fracture stress, σ_f, of a metal does not vary as much with temperature as does the yield stress, σ_y. In Figure 5.1(a), curve (i) shows the variation of σ_f with temperature, while curves (ii) and (iii) show the variation of σ_y with temperature for a body-centred cubic metal. Curve (ii) is the effect for slow rates of strain and curve (iii) applies under conditions of high rates of strain (impact loading). At low rates of strain, $\sigma_f < \sigma_y$ at all temperatures below T_1, while for impact conditions $\sigma_f < \sigma_y$ at temperatures below T_2. In other words, at temperatures between T_1 and T_2 the metal will show ductile behaviour at low rates of strain but will be brittle under impact conditions. Figure 5.1(b) shows the relationship between impact strength and temperature, as measured in a Charpy test, for a body centred cubic metal.

Failure of parts of low-carbon steel structures by brittle fracture had occurred since steels were first used, but it was only during the 1940s that the

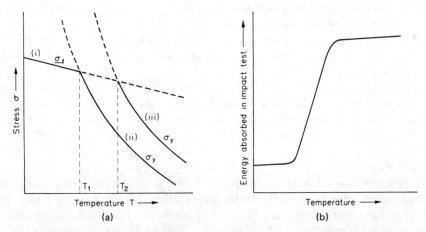

Figure 5.1 (a) Variation of σ_f, and σ_y with temperature for a b.c.c. metal: (i) $\sigma_f - T$; (ii) $\sigma_y - T$ for slow strain rate; (iii) $\sigma_y - T$ for fast strain rate. (b) Impact strength against temperature for a metal showing ductile–brittle transition.

Figure 5.2 Charpy impact fractures of mild steel; (a) sample tested at 20°C (typical ductile fracture with fibrous surface); (b) sample tested at −25°C (typical brittle fracture of cleavage type).

problem became highlighted and received considerable publicity. This coincided with the introduction of all-welded ship hull construction. Previously if brittle fracture occurred in a portion of a ship's plating, the fracture would be arrested at a line of rivets, or at the edge of the plate. In an all-welded ship, the hull effectively consists of a single continuous plate and brittle fracture, once started, could propagate catastrophically. Certain alloying elements in the steel affect the ductile–brittle transition temperature. The transition temperature is reduced by the presence of manganese and nickel, but is increased by carbon, nitrogen and phosphorus.

5.3 Notch Impact Tests

Notch impact tests are widely used in industry as acceptance checks. They are relatively simple and are easy and rapid to conduct. The general principle of the tests is that a test specimen, containing a milled notch, is struck by a fast moving hammer and the energy that is absorbed in fracturing the test-piece is measured.

As mentioned in Section 5.2, the ductile–brittle transition temperature is considerably higher for impact loading conditions than for slow strain-rate conditions. It is comparatively easy to determine the transition temperature range under impact loading conditions as there is a very large difference between the energy required to cause ductile and brittle fractures in this type of test.

Another major use of notch impact testing is to determine whether heat treatments have been carried out successfully. This type of test has the advantage of revealing a tendency to brittleness that is not revealed by either a standard tensile test or hardness test. This is illustrated by the data in Table 5.1 for samples of a low alloy steel subject to temper brittleness.

Table 5.1 Material with similar tensile properties but different notch-impact strengths, according to condition

Composition (per cent)	Condition	Tensile strength (MN/m^2)	Elongation on 50 mm (per cent)	Charpy impact value (kJ/m^2)
C 0.3 Ni 3.2 Cr 1.0	Hardened, tempered and cooled rapidly after tempering	855	28.6	1050
	Hardened, tempered and cooled slowly after tempering	836	26.5	120

Notch-impact test results should not be used alone. They should be used in conjunction with the results of other tests, including the standard tensile and hardness tests. The two types of notch impact test most widely used in Britain are the *Charpy* test and the *Izod* test and these are described in the next two Sections.

5.4 The Izod Notch Impact Test

The Izod test machine consists of a heavy pendulum fixed in a rigid frame. The pendulum, of mass 27.24 kg (60 lb), is allowed to swing from a height of 0.61 m (2 ft). The velocity of the pendulum at the base of its swing is about 3.5 m/s. At the bottom of its swing the pendulum strikes the notched bar test-piece, which is rigidly mounted in a vice. A proportion of the striking energy is used to fracture the test-piece and the height of the follow-through swing of the pendulum is noted. The actual value of energy used to fracture a test-piece is indicated on a scale by a maximum indicating pointer which is moved forward by the moving pendulum. The notch impact value is quoted as the energy for fracture per unit area, the preferred units being kilojoules per square metre (kJ/m^2). The area which is taken is the effective cross-sectional area of the test-piece, excluding the notch. As an example, a sample of 10 mm $\times$ 10 mm cross- section with a V-notch of 2 mm depth which absorbed 24 J of energy in fracturing would be recorded as having an impact value of $(24/80) \times 10^6 = 300$ kJ/m^2.

The standard test-piece dimensions are either of 10 mm square section or 11.4 mm diameter circular section with a 2 mm deep milled V-notch. (BS.131 Part 1 (1961)). The test-piece may possess a single notch or have three notches, milled at 90° angular intervals. (Figure 5.4) The triple notch

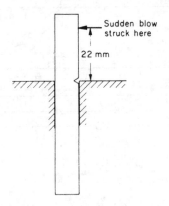

Figure 5.3 Izod test-piece arrangement.

test-piece permits three impact values to be obtained from the same sample with the test-piece being raised and reset in the vice after the first and second determinations. It is important that the test-piece be located accurately in the vice and a special positioning gauge is used to ensure this. The results of notch-impact tests may be subject to considerable variation and it is advisable to take the mean of six or more individual values.

The Izod test is a recognised test for plastics materials as well as for metals (refer to BS 2782, Part 3, Method 350 (1984)). It is recommended that the mean of ten impact readings be taken to give a representative result for plastics materials.

One disadvantage of the Izod test method is that it is not as suitable as the Charpy method for determining the impact values of materials at temperatures other than ambient. If test-pieces are taken from an oven or refri-

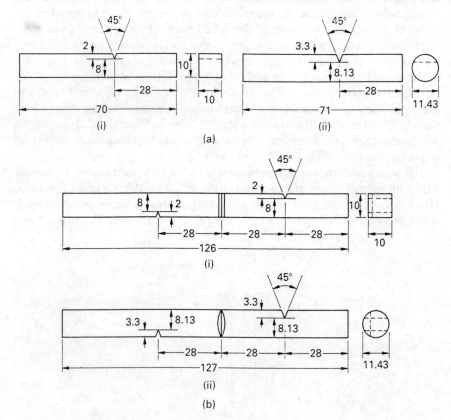

All dimensions in mm

Figure 5.4 Izod metal test specimen dimensions: (a) single V-notch test-pieces, (i) square section, (ii) circular section; (b) triple V-notch test-pieces (i) square section, (ii) circular section.

gerator their temperature may fall or rise considerably and by some
unknown amount, during the time taken to position them correctly within
the vice on the machine.

Very brittle materials, such as cast iron, may be tested in the un-notched
form and a separate standard, BS 1349, relates to this method.

5.5 The Charpy Notch Impact Test

The main difference between the Charpy method and the Izod test is that in
the Charpy test the test-piece is mounted as a simply supported beam and
the impact blow occurs at mid-span directly behind the notch. (Figure 5.5
(b)) The pendulum energy at the base of its swing in the standard Charpy
machine is 320 J although smaller capacity machines are available also. The
velocity of the pendulum of a 320 J machine at the base of its swing is
considerably greater than the striking velocity of the standard Izod machine
and is about 5.3 m/s.

Charpy test-pieces may be produced with either a V-notch or a U-notch,
and the standard specimen dimensions for metals are given in Figure 5.5(a).
BS 131, Part 2 (1972) and BS 131, Part 3 (1972) refer to the Charpy test for
metals for V-notch testing and U-notch testing respectively.

The Charpy test method is suitable for use with plastics materials as well
and BS 2782, Part 3, method 359(1984) covers the notch-impact testing of
plastics by this method. As is the case for the Izod test, it is recommended
that ten specimens be tested to obtain a representative result for plastics
materials. There is no number given in the appropriate standard for the
number of metal samples which should be tested in order to achieve a
representative result but, in the author's experience, at least nine or ten
determinations should be made.

The Charpy test can be used successfully to determine the notch impact
properties at temperatures other than ambient. Because the test-piece does
not have to be clamped in a vice but is merely resting on support ledges, it is
possible to transfer hot or cold samples from an adjacent oven or refri-

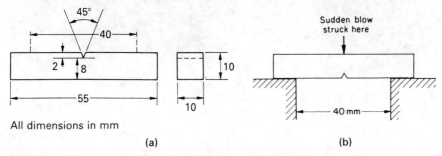

All dimensions in mm

(a)   (b)

Figure 5.5 (a) Charpy metal test piece dimensions, (b) Test-piece arrangement.

gerator, place in the machine and complete the test within a matter of seconds rather than minutes. There will be only a very small rise or fall in the temperature of the test-piece in this short interval.

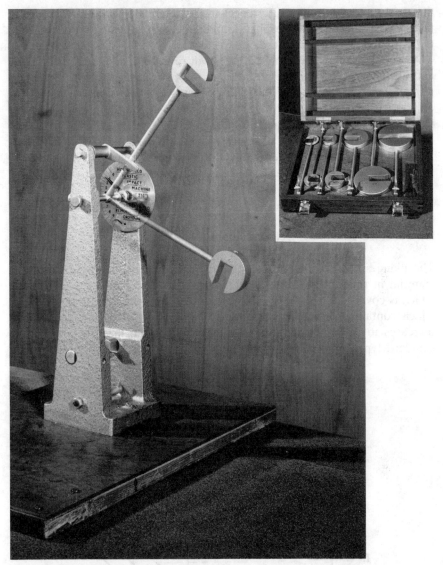

Figure 5.7 Miniature Charpy (2. 7 J) machine (double exposure photograph) with range of penduli (inset).

5.6 Notch Impact Values

The results obtained from Charpy and Izod tests are roughly comparable for samples with notches of the same geometry, despite the differing impact velocities. Notch geometry, particularly the root radius of the notch, is an important factor. Comparatively minor variations in the radius at the tip of the notch can cause major differences in the notch impact value. The size of test-piece also affects the results. An increase in size leads to a decrease in the critical energy per unit area of fracture.

As stated earlier, notch impact tests will reveal a tendency to brittleness and are very useful for the determination of the ductile–brittle transition temperature. The results of this type of test, while informative, tend to be qualitative in nature rather than quantitative and, by themselves, provide insufficient data for the engineer to design with confidence for the avoidance of brittle or fast fractures in structures. The design engineer requires further information, namely quantitative data on fracture toughness. This property is the resistance of the material to fast crack propagation.

5.7 Fracture Toughness Determination

The plane strain fracture toughness, K_{IC}, is the critical toughness of the material in relation to mode I opening of a crack. (Figure 5.8) The test, which is covered by BS 5447 (1977), involves applying load to a test-piece which contains a crack and noting the amount of force required to give increases in the crack length. The test-piece, which may be one of two standard types (Figure 5.9) is machined with a milled notch and, prior to

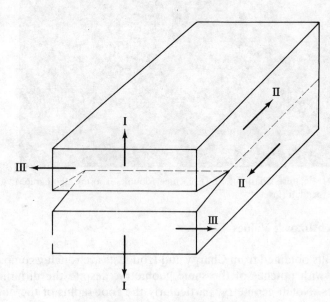

Figure 5.8 Mode 1 opening of a crack.

testing for fracture toughness, a small crack is generated from the root of the notch. Crack generation is generally brought about by a fatigue process, i.e. subjecting the test-piece to cyclical stress.

The SEN type test-piece is subjected to bending using a three-point loading system while the CTS type test-piece is stressed by means of a tensile force acting normally to the direction of the notch and crack and along the centre line of the two holes in the specimen. The full details of the tests and the analysis of results to obtain a value of K_{IC} are beyond the scope of this volume, but they are detailed in BS 5447 (1977).

5.8 Crack Opening Displacement Testing

The fracture toughness tests for the determination of K_{IC} mentioned in Section 5.7 are used for metals in which the pre-formed cracked extends under load with little, if any, plastic deformation of the material. Values of K_{IC} cannot be determined successfully when the material shows considerable plastic deformation as well as crack growth, when force is applied. In these circumstances, another parameter is determined, namely the crack opening displacement, or COD. COD is the opening, or widening, of the crack at a position corresponding to the original tip of the crack. The preferred test-piece for this test-procedure is the SEN type with a three-point loading system. The crack opening displacement is obtained through the use of clip gauges. A critical value of COD, as measured on a test-piece, can be used to calculate the relationship between fracture stress and defect size in a structure. The details of this type of test are given in BS 5762 (1979).

5.9 Self Assessment Questions

5.1 What is meant by the terms 'ductile failure' and 'brittle failure'?

5.2 What is meant by the term 'notch-ductility transition temperature'?

5.3 What are the main reasons for using notch-impact tests?

5.4 What is the major advantage of the Charpy test over the Izod test?

5.5 A notch-impact test sample of 10 mm square cross-section with a standard milled V-notch 2 mm deep absorbs 115 J of energy in fracture. How should this test result be expressed?

5.6 In what way does fracture toughness differ from notch-impact toughness?

5.7 What form of test is used to determine the fracture toughness parameters for a metal which may show significant plastic deformation during crack propagation?

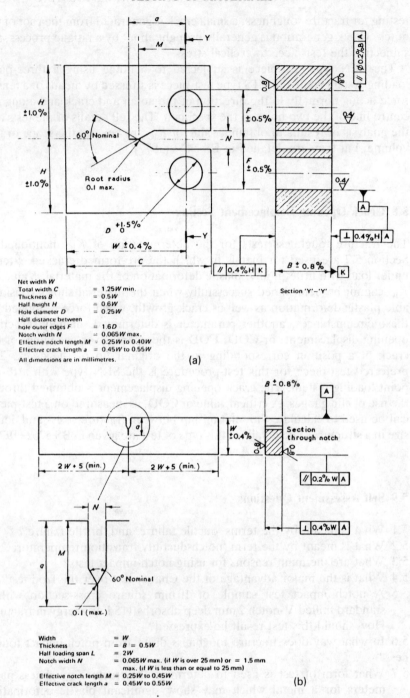

Net width W
Total width C = 1.25W min.
Thickness B = 0.5W
Half height H = 0.6W
Hole diameter D = 0.25W
Half distance between
hole outer edges F = 1.6D
Notch width N = 0.065W max.
Effective notch length M = 0.25W to 0.40W
Effective crack length a = 0.45W to 0.55W

All dimensions are in millimetres.

(a)

Width = W
Thickness = B = 0.5W
Half loading span L = 2W
Notch width N = 0.065W max. (if W is over 25 mm) or = 1.5 mm
max. (if W is less than or equal to 25 mm)
Effective notch length M = 0.25W to 0.45W
Effective crack length a = 0.45W to 0.55W

(b)

Figure 5.9 (a) Compact tensile test-piece (CTS), (b) Single edge notch test-piece (SEN).

6

Fatigue and Fatigue Testing

6.1 Fatigue

Probably the greatest proportion of failures of components or structures in service can be ascribed to failure by fatigue. This is a type of failure caused by the action of varying stresses below the short-term static tensile or torsional strength of the material.

Examination of a fatigue fracture surface shows two distinct parts. There is a smooth portion and the crystalline fracture zone (Figure 6.1). Usually a series of curved lines, giving mussel shell type markings, can be seen on the smooth section of the fracture surface. These indicate that crack propagation has taken the form of step growth from the point of initiation. This part

Figure 6.1 Fracture surface of large diameter shaft which has failed by fatigue, with crack initiation from point A. This shows clearly the smooth zone with conchoidal, or shell-like, markings and the brittle fracture zone.

of the surface has been worn smooth by the relative motion between the two surfaces of the crack during very many loading cycles. Finally, when the fatigue crack, or cracks, have grown to such an extent that the area of unbroken section is no longer sufficient to sustain the load, fracture propagates rapidly across the remainder. This final portion of the fracture surface generally has the crystalline appearance typical of a brittle failure.

When metal samples are tested to determine the fatigue characteristics, the test conditions often involve the application of an alternating stress cycle with a mean stress of zero. The results of such tests are plotted in the form of an $S - \log N$ curve, where S is the maximum stress in the cycle and N is the number of stress cycles to failure. (Figure 6.2). Most steels show an $S - \log N$ curve of type (i) in the figure with a definite fatigue limit. This fatigue limit for steels occurs at about one-half of the value of static tensile strength after some 10^6 or 10^7 cycles. This means that if the maximum stress in any cycle does not exceed the fatigue limit then failure by fatigue should never occur. Non-ferrous metals do not show a definite fatigue limit and give $S - \log N$ curves similar to that shown in Figure 6.2 (ii).

Although the maximum stress in conditions which lead to fatigue are below the nominal elastic limit of the material, it has been established that some plastic deformation by slip does take place. With continued cyclic stressing slip bands appear on the material and there are some extrusive and

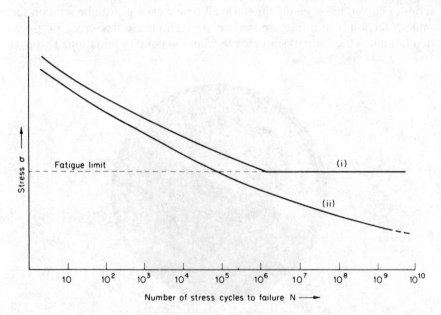

Figure 6.2 $S - \log N$ curves for (i) metal showing fatigue limit and (ii) metal showing no fatigue limit.

intrusive effects at these slip bands (Figure 6.3). These extrusions and intrusions are extremely small, being of the order of one micron (1 μm) in size.

Once an intrusion has formed, it can act as the focus for the generation of a fatigue crack. The intrusion, with a very small root radius, acts as a point of stress concentration and a crack slowly propagates through the material until, eventually, the remaining sound portion of the cross-section is too small to sustain the maximum load in any one stress cycle and sudden fracture occurs. The presence of surface scratches, micro-cracks or geometrical features, such as key-ways or sharp changes in section, can act as points or areas of stress concentration and result in the early initiation of fatigue cracks. In the foregoing sentences, it is implied that fatigue crack initiation is a surface phenomenon. It is true that in very many cases fatigue cracks commence at the surface but it must be recognised that many examples of failure by fatigue occur in rotating parts, such as axles and shafts, with loading arrangements such that the maximum stress levels are always at the component surface. When a component is subjected to direct axial stressing and there is a uniform stress distribution across the section, fatigue cracking may commence at some point or points within the section.

6.2 Factors Affecting Fatigue

There are many factors which affect the performance of a material or component in conditions likely to lead to failure by fatigue. These include the type of loading and load cycling, the surface condition, component design and the nature of the environment.

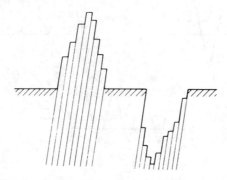

Figure 6.3 Intrusions and extrusions formed in the early stages of fatigue.

Type of stress

The formation of small intrusions and extrusions by a plastic slip process, as outlined in the preceding section, is brought about by the action of resolved shear stresses. In consequence, the fatigue strength of a material subject to torsional stress cycles is lower than that determined for cycles of direct stress. Once a fatigue crack has been initiated, the rate of crack propagation is affected by tensile and compressive stresses. Tension tends to open up the crack tip and cause growth while compression tends to retard crack growth.

Type of loading cycle

The type of cyclic stressing to which a component may be subjected in service can be classified as alternating, repeating or fluctuating (Figure 6.4). In an alternating stress cycle, the value of the mean stress, σ_m, is zero. In a fluctuating stress cycle, the mean stress, σ_m, has some value other than zero and in a repeating cycle the minimum stress, σ_{min}, is zero. The stress range of a cycle, $\Delta\sigma$, is $(\sigma_{max} - \sigma_{min})$, the cyclic stress amplitude, $\sigma_a = \frac{1}{2}(\sigma_{max} - \sigma_{min})$, and the mean cycle stress, $\sigma_m = \frac{1}{2}(\sigma_{max} + \sigma_{min})$.

The type of $S - \log N$ curve shown in Figure 6.2 (i) is obtained most usually from tests involving alternating stress cycles (in which the mean stress, σ_m, is zero). The *fatigue limit*, σ_{FL}, is quoted as the value of tensile stress in such an alternating cycle and so the range of stress in the cycle, $\Delta\sigma$, is twice the fatigue limit. Where the mean stress is not zero, the maximum range of stress which can be tolerated will differ from that for an alternating cycle. When the mean stress is tensile, the maximum range of stress is reduced. Several equations of an empirical nature have been proposed to

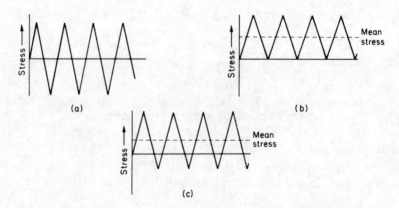

Figure 6.4 Types of stress cycle: (a) alternating; (b) repeating; (c) fluctuating.

give the relationships between stress ranges, mean stresses and fatigue life. They are

1. The modified Goodman equation:

$$\frac{\sigma_m}{\sigma_{FL}} + \frac{\sigma_m}{\sigma_{TS}} = 1$$

2. The Gerber parabolic equation:

$$\frac{\sigma_m}{\sigma_{FL}} + \left(\frac{\sigma_m}{\sigma_{TS}}\right)^2 = 1$$

3. The Soderberg equation:

$$\frac{\sigma_m}{\sigma_{FL}} + \frac{\sigma_m}{\sigma_y} = 1$$

In these equations, σ_{FL} is the fatigue strength as determined in tests with a mean stress of zero, σ_{TS} is the tensile strength, and σ_y is the yield strength of the material. These empirical laws are used to a limited extent despite their uncertainties.

Rate of cycling

In many instances, the rate of load cycling does not have an effect on fatigue life, at least, up to frequencies of about 150 Hz. At higher frequencies, there appears to be a small increase in fatigue strength. This increase is of the order of 10 per cent at very high frequencies (up to 15000 Hz). The term *low cycle fatigue* is used to describe situations in which the cycle frequency is extremely low. An example of low cycle fatigue is the repeated pressurisation of an aircraft cabin where one cycle is completed in one flight of the aircraft. Low cycle fatigue may lead to failure after something of the order of 10^4 to 10^5 cycles. The disastrous failure of the Comet airliners in the 1950s were examples of pressure cabin failures due to low cycle fatigue, in this case coupled with a serious design fault, namely the stress-raising effect at the sharp corners of rectangular windows in the fuselage structure.

Surface condition and surface defects

The condition of the surface of a component will have a major influence on its fatigue life. Surface roughness or the presence of surface scratches can act as points of stress concentration. Fatigue is highly stress sensitive and the presence of any stress raising feature will accelerate the initiation of a fatigue crack. The effect of a surface scratch or other surface defect will not be the same for all materials. Ductile metals are less sensitive to these surface effects than brittle metals. In a ductile metal, plastic flow at the base of a scratch may increase the root radius and lower the stress raising effect of the flaw. The relationship between the stress intensity factor, ΔK, size of a surface defect and the cyclic stress range is given by $\Delta K = C \Delta\sigma \, (\pi d)^{1/2}$, where $\Delta\sigma$ is the cyclic stress range, d is the depth of a surface flaw (or depth of a trough in a machined surface profile) and C is a material constant. Catastrophic failure will occur when ΔK reaches a critical value, this value being a function of the material.

The fatigue life of a component may be improved by *peening* the surface. Peening involves lightly hammering the surface of the component with a round-nosed hammer or bombarding the surface with small steel pellets. The treatment induces residual compressive stresses within the surface layers and the initiation of fatigue cracks is delayed or prevented. Other surface treatments which can improve the fatigue life by introducing compressive stresses in the surface layers are surface hardening treatments such as carburising and nitriding and some electro-plated coatings.

Design considerations

As mentioned above, fatigue is stress-sensitive and, hence, the presence of any stress-raising features in the design of a component will influence the fatigue life. Any change of shape or cross-section will cause a local concentration of stress. Splines, key-ways and oil holes in shafts are often points at which fatigue commences. The stress-raising effect of a change in section is more a function of the severity of the change rather than the total magnitude of the change and the provision of a generous radius at the change in section will help minimise the incidence of fatigue. It is worth noting that the point of fatigue crack initiation in the Comet aircraft disasters was at the square corner of a fuselage window and that these disasters may not have occurred had the design incorporated oval windows, as is the practice today.

Environmental effects

If conditions are such that corrosion can occur, not only is the fatigue limit very greatly reduced but also the rate of corrosion is increased. For some materials, including some steels, there is no fatigue limit in a corrosive environment and failure will occur eventually even when the level of stress is very low.

Many service conditions may involve a part being subjected to a series of differing stress cycles, with different cyclical amplitudes. Miner's law of cumulative fatigue is an empirical rule which can be used to estimate the fatigue life of a component when subjected to a series of different loading cycles. For example, if stressed for n_1 cycles in a regime which would cause failure in a total of N_1 cycles and for n_2 cycles in a regime where failure would occur after N_2 cycles, then n_1/N_1 of the fatigue life of the component would be used up in the first case and the fraction n_2/N_2 of the fatigue life used in the second instance. Miner's rule can be expressed by stating that failure will occur when $\Sigma(n/N) = 1$.

Failure by a fatigue process is not confined to metals. Materials such as concrete and polymers can fail due to a fatigue process and, as with metals, the number of stress cycles to cause failure is increased as the maximum stress in the load cycles is decreased, but there does not appear to be a definite fatigue limit with these materials. There are difficulties in the fatigue testing of polymers because the temperature of a test-piece tends to increase in the course of a test because of the low thermal conductivity and high damping capacity of these materials.

6.3 Fatigue Testing

A component or structure in service may be subjected to fluctuating or alternating cycles of stress but rarely can it be found that one constant type of loading cycle applies during the whole of the life of a component. Laboratory fatigue tests tend to be based on some uniform type of stress cycle be it alternating, repeating or fluctuating (Figure 6.4) applied in a systematic manner. Very many different machines have been designed for fatigue testing and there is no standardisation of test-pieces. A British Standard (BS 3518) exists but this makes recommendations on general principles and points of good practice to be maintained in the preparation of test-pieces and the conduct of tests rather than detailing standard tests. BS 3518 part 1 (1962) covers the general principles of fatigue testing while Parts 2, 3 and 4 deal with rotating bending testing, direct stress testing and torsion testing respectively.

There are several tests based on the rotating bending principle. Of these, the Wöhler rotating cantilever and the four-point bending system are used widely (Figure 6.5). In both of these tests, at any instant in time, one element of the surface of the test-piece is stressed in tension while that element of the surface diametrically opposed to the first is stressed in compression. During one complete revolution of the test-piece any one section of the surface will go through a complete stress cycle, with a mean stress of zero.

Direct stress fatigue testing involves loading a test-piece in both tension and compression. The test-piece used resembles a tensile test-piece in form. It is a requirement that the loading to be uniaxial. The comparatively simple self-aligning grips used in tensile testing machines are not suitable for fatigue testing. Test-pieces generally have screw-thread ends and the test-piece holders are housed within fixed precision guides to ensure that loading in both tension and compression will be purely axial. One advantage of the direct stress type of test, as opposed to the rotating bend test, is that the loading cycle may be set so that the mean stress is not zero.

It is important that fatigue test-pieces be prepared with a smooth polished surface. Specimens are fine machined to the appropriate shape and dimensions and then polished. The final stage of polishing should be with 600 grade silicon carbide paper, with the grit lines running longitudinally along the test-piece surface, to give a surface texture of less than 0.125 μm (5 μ-inch) CLA. It is recommended that the cyclic rate for fatigue testing be between 50 and 120 Hz.

6.4 Significance of Test Results

The results of fatigue tests are shown generally in the form of S–log N curves and it is important, when presenting fatigue results that the method of stressing, type of machine used, test-piece dimensions and the cycle frequency be quoted. Data may also be presented in tabulated form. The terms *fatigue life* and *endurance* refer to the number of cycles to failure and normally the values of endurance are 10^6 cycles for structural steels and 10^7 cycles for other steels and non-ferrous metals. The terms *fatigue strength* and *endurance limit* are used to denote the maximum level of stress which will give a finite life, i.e. no failure in some specified number of cycles.

There are many variables in fatigue testing. There may be considerable scatter in fatigue test results, even when all test-pieces are produced in controlled conditions with uniform polished surfaces. The test conditions in

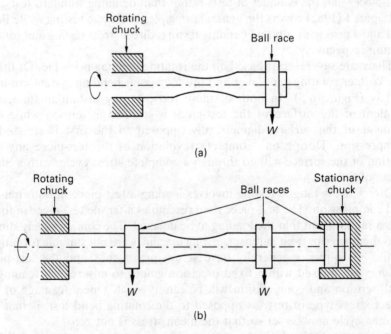

Figure 6.5 Principle of rotating bending fatigue tests: (a) Wöhler rotating cantilever test; (b) four-point bending rotating test.

laboratory fatigue testing usually involve standard uniform loading conditions and so it is difficult to correlate laboratory fatigue test results with behaviour in service. In consequence, it is difficult to use fatigue test results directly in design. Because of this, it is necessary, on occasions, to devise and conduct fatigue tests to failure on complete engineering structures. Following the pressure cabin failures of early Comet aircraft, in the 1950s a complete Comet air-frame was tested to destruction in a special test rig at the Royal Aircraft Establishment, Farnborough. The test simulated both the cabin pressure changes and the wing flexing that occurred during each flight. Since that date, a similar test to destruction has been made on one airframe of every civil transport aircraft type destined for service. This has been a requirement of the airworthiness certification procedure.

6.5 Self Assessment Questions

6.1 What is meant by the term 'fatigue limit'?

6.2 Why does peening the surface of a component tend to improve its fatigue life?

6.3 It is recommended that the surface of a fatigue test specimen has a surface texture of better than 0.125 µm CLA. What are the reasons for this?

6.4 Fatigue tests, using alternating stress cycles, on a steel which has a tensile strength of 400 MPa and a tensile yield strength of 320 MPa show that there is a fatigue limit of 180 MPa at 10^6 cycles. If further tests are carried out using fluctuating load cycles with a mean tensile stress of 30 MPa, what will be the approximate maximum stress range which can be used, if failure before 10^6 cycles is to be avoided?

6.5 Fatigue failure of stressed rotating engineering components such as shafts and axles often occurs at keyways, oil-holes, or positions where the sectional dimensions change. Why is this so and what steps can be taken to minimise this tendency?

6.6 State the principle of the Wöhler fatigue test.

6.7 What are the main advantages and disadvantages of rotating beam fatigue tests?

7

Creep and Creep Testing

7.1 Creep

Creep is the continued slow straining of a material under constant load. Another phenomenon, related to creep, is *relaxation*. This is the reduction in the level of stress within a material with time when the strain is constant. Both creep and relaxation are of consequence with many thermoplastics at ordinary temperatures but do not become significant for ceramics, glasses and the majority of metallic materials until the temperature is raised. For metals, this is at temperatures in excess of 0.5 T_m, where T_m is the melting point in Kelvin.

A typical creep curve for a metal is shown in Figure 7.1. It will be seen that the curve comprises three distinct portions. These are *primary*, or *transient creep, secondary* or *steady state creep* and *tertiary creep*. This last phase leads to rapid failure.

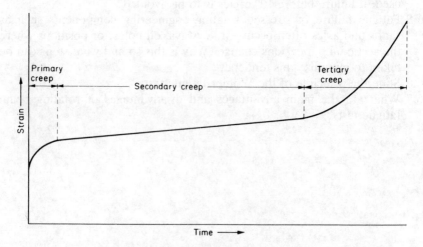

Figure 7.1 Typical creep curve for a metal.

Primary creep in metals is probably entirely due to the normal process of slip, and strain hardening occurs which quickly reduces the rate of strain. When the period of transient creep is over, the material continues to strain very slowly at a constant rate. The secondary creep rate is temperature dependent. Secondary creep is a thermally activated process and the variation of creep strain rate, $d\epsilon/dt$, with temperature is in accordance with the Arrhenius law and can be expressed as

$$\text{Creep rate } \frac{d\epsilon}{dt} = A \exp \left(\frac{B}{T}\right)$$

where T is the temperature (K) and A and B are constants. One of the theories that has been advanced for the process of steady-state creep is that of dislocation climb and the continued slow movement of dislocations under the action of a constant stress. There is also evidence that, at very high temperatures, the creep process involves slow viscous flow of grain boundary material. Generally, the rate of strain in secondary creep is small and continued steady straining will occur over a long period of time. The change from secondary to tertiary creep is caused by the intervention of some other effect such as the formation of small internal cavities or localised necking of the material. When such effects occur, the effective stress in the fissured or necked zone will increase and cause an increase in the rate of strain. This is the onset of tertiary creep and, usually, there is a rapid acceleration in the creep strain rate and this leads to failure.

As mentioned earlier, creep is highly temperature-dependent and the effects of increasing temperature, with loading conditions maintained at constant level, on creep rates are shown in Figure 7.2. At low temperatures,

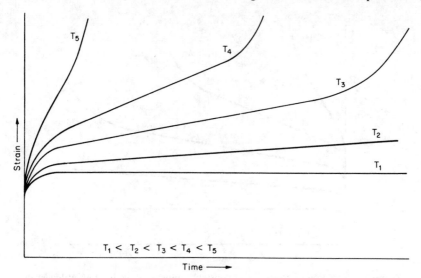

Figure 7.2 Variation of creep rate with temperature – constant load.

there may be transient creep only while, at very high temperatures, primary creep may merge directly into tertiary creep.

Secondary creep rates are also stress-dependent. An increase in stress, σ, will increase the rate of creep strain, $d\epsilon/dt$, following the relationship:

$$d\epsilon/dt = C\,\sigma^n$$

where C and n are constants of the material. Figure 7.3 shows a series of creep curves for a material at constant temperature but with different loads.

Relaxation

When a material is strained by a specific amount and thereafter the dimensions remain unchanged, the stress developed within the material will reduce with time. This is termed relaxation and, like creep, is temperature sensitive. The general form of relaxation curves is shown in Figure 7.4. It is important to have relaxation data for materials such as steels to be used for the manufacture of bolts for use at elevated temperatures. Stress relaxation with time could make a bolt become slack, even to the point of danger, and it is necessary to know at what time intervals the bolts should be re-tightened.

7.2 Presentation of Creep Data

A creep curve of the type shown in Figure 7.1 is the result of one single test and gives the variation of strain with time for one value of load at one

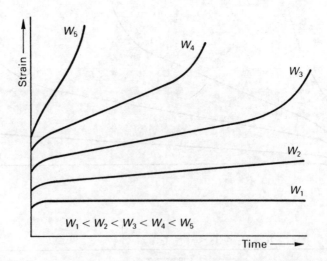

Figure 7.3 Variation of creep rate at constant temperature with different loads, W.

constant temperature. A single result of this type is of little value and very many creep tests must be conducted on a material covering a range of temperatures and loads if a full picture of the creep characteristics of the alloy is to be obtained.

There are several items of quantitative information that can be derived from a single creep test result of the type shown in Figure 7.1. These are

(a) the time required to produce some specified value of strain,
(b) the creep strain which occurs in some specified time,
(c) the rate of strain during steady-state creep.
(d) the time at which tertiary creep commences, and
(e) the time necessary for failure by fracture.

It is customary to plot the results of very many creep tests in the form of summary charts designed to show the effects of variations in both stress and temperature on some particular parameter. The main parameters which are shown in this way are the conditions to cause rupture in some given time, the conditions to give some specified amount of total strain in a given time and the maximum stress/temperature conditions if the steady-state creep rate is not to exceed some specific value. A brief description of these various types of summary curve is given below.

Stress-rupture curves

Much creep data on materials is plotted in the form of stress-rupture curves and the summary curves show the levels of both stress and temperature which will cause failure in a given time. The given time values generally taken are 100 hours, 1000 hours, 10000 hours or, occasionally, 100000

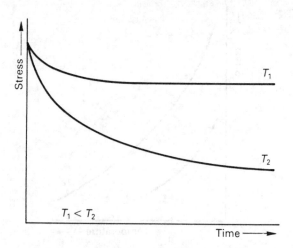

Figure 7.4 Form of relaxation curves at two different temperatures.

hours. These figures show the extremely long nature of creep rates. 10 000 hours is 417 days while 100 000 hours is between 11 and 12 years. The individual values of stress for rupture may be obtained from a series of full creep tests in which strain is measured or may be obtained from special tests in which strain is not recorded (Section 7.5). The general form of stress-rupture data presentation is shown in Figures 7.5 and 7.8.

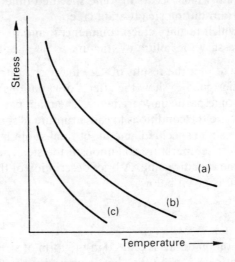

Figure 7.5 Summary curves showing stress–temperature values for rupture in (a) 100 hours, (b) 1000 hours and (c) 10 000 hours.

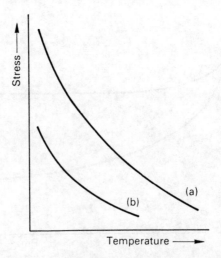

Figure 7.6 Form of summary creep strength curves: (a) stress to give strain of 0.001 in 1000 hours; (b) stress to give strain of 0.001 in 10 000 hours.

Specific creep strain curves

In this type of summary curve, the data which is plotted is the value of stress and temperature which will give some specified amount of strain in a given time. In many cases, the amount of strain which is specified is 0.001 (0.1 per cent). This type of curve is shown in Figure 7.6.

Limiting creep strain rate curves

In many instances, a designer will wish to know the limiting conditions of stress and temperature if the secondary creep strain rate is not to exceed a certain value. A typical value of secondary creep rate used is 10^{-5}/hour. In order to ensure that the primary, or transient creep stage is complete it is customary to determine the creep rate after a lengthy period of time, say 1000 hours.

7.3 Creep Resistant Alloys

It was stated in Section 7.1 that the mechanism of creep in metals, at least at some temperatures, involved the slow continued movement of dislocations. Consequently, the presence of any microstructural feature which will hinder the movement of dislocations will tend to increase the creep strength of the material. One of the important methods used in the development of strong creep-resistant metals and alloys for extended service at elevated temperatures is dispersion strengthening.

The development of the aero gas turbine, with its requirement for materials capable of operating at high levels of stress at high temperatures, has been the stimulus for much research into creep, into the development of creep resistant alloys and into the development of new forming processes in

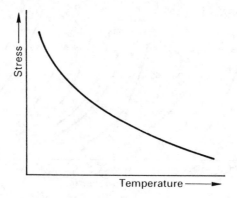

Figure 7.7 Form of summary creep strength curve showing stress to cause creep rate of 10^{-5}/hour after 1000 hours.

order to obtain the best possible properties. These developments, together with the introduction of turbine blade cooling, have made it possible for turbine entry temperatures to be increased by some 400 °C (from 700 °C to 1100 °C) over a twenty-five year period from 1960, permitting the design and manufacture of power plants with much improved thermal efficiencies. The so-called *superalloys* are based on nickel but contain many alloying elements and are very complex in structure. Some alloying elements will enter solid solution and strengthen the matrix while others tend to form intermetallic compounds and carbides. When these compounds are present in the structure in large quantity in a highly dispersed state, it will be extremely difficult for dislocation movement to occur within the material, so giving a highly creep-resistant material. Processing technology development has taken place alongside alloy-composition developments. The development of directional solidification for the production of cast turbine blades made it possible to make blades with microstructures in which the crystal grains are aligned in the direction of maximum direct stress and having very few, if any, grain boundaries normal to this direction. This gave blades with improved creep properties, particularly at very high temperatures, where viscous grain boundary flow becomes a major factor in creep. A recent and logical development from this was the production of single crystal turbine blades. A series of 1000 hour stress-rupture curves for a range of materials is shown in Figure 7.8. The alloy DS M002 is a directionally solidified complex nickel alloy. It will be seen in the figure that the creep strengths of directionally solidified and single crystal materials are significantly higher than those of conventionally processed superalloys.

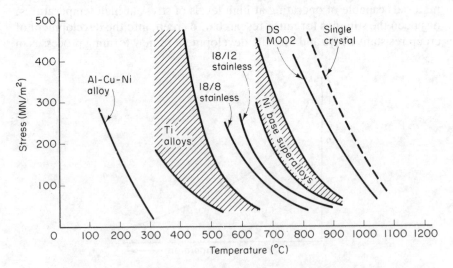

Figure 7.8 1000 hours stress-rupture curves for various materials.

7.4 Creep Testing

Almost all creep testing is conducted in the tensile mode and the test specimens are similar in form to those used in tensile testing (see Section 3.4). Test-pieces for tensile creep testing may be of either circular or rectangular cross-section but there are no standard sizes. The actual dimensions of the test-pieces used will depend upon the type of creep testing machine used.

The basic requirements for a creep testing machine are

(a) that it must possess means for applying and maintaining a constant tensile load,
(b) there must be a furnace capable of keeping the temperature of the test-piece at the desired value to within very close limits,
(c) there should be means for the accurate measurement of test-piece extension.

This last requirement is not necessary if the equipment is to be used only for the determination of stress-to-rupture data.

Tensile creep test machines are designed so that the test-piece is mounted vertically and, generally, the axial load is applied to the specimen holder by dead weights and a lever system. It is essential that the temperature of the test-piece be very closely controlled for the duration of a test and that the temperature be uniform along the length of the specimen. The usual arrangement is to have an electric resistance tubular furnace mounted on the frame of the testing machine and moveable in the vertical plane. The furnace can then be moved up and down on guides to place it either in position around the specimen, or clear of the specimen to allow for insertion or removal of the test-piece and setting of the extensometer system. The furnace should be considerably longer than the test-piece to ensure that the whole length of the specimen can be maintained at a uniform temperature. BS 3500 (1969) covers the standard conditions for creep testing and specifies the very close temperature tolerances required. Temperatures must be maintained to within $\pm 2\,^\circ$C for tests at temperatures up to 600 $^\circ$C, to $\pm 2.5\,^\circ$C for tests at temperatures between 600 $^\circ$C and 800 $^\circ$C and to $\pm 3\,^\circ$C for temperatures between 800 $^\circ$C and 1000 $^\circ$C. In order to achieve these conditions, not only must the furnace be carefully constructed and controlled but thermocouples and temperature measuring instruments need to be highly accurate and sensitive. Furnaces for creep test work generally have several zones, each of which can be individually controlled, in order to compensate for the normal temperature drop which occurs at the ends of the furnace tube. Several accurate thermocouples must be positioned along the gauge length of a test-piece and the sensitivities of the temperature-measuring instruments should be such that differences of 0.5 $^\circ$C or less can be determined.

Accurate measurement of strain is necessary during the course of a creep test, except in the case of creep stress-to-rupture tests, and generally the extensometers used are of the mirror type (Figure 3.7) capable of measuring extensions of the order 10^{-3} or 10^{-4} mm. Extension rods made from a heat-resistant alloy connect the gripping points at the test-piece to the extensometer outside the furnace. Usually, the more sensitive an extensometer is, the smaller will be the total extension that it is capable of measuring. Most extensometers used for creep work are adapted to have a resetting facility in order to extend the measuring range and enable large extensions to be read with high accuracy. The securing of the extensometer extension arms to the test-piece may pose some problems. Knife-edge contacts may be used to attach the extensometer arms to the gauge length within the waisted section of the test-piece. The contacts have to be attached extremely tightly if they are not to loosen during the course of a test, particularly if the test temperature is very high. Extreme tightening of knife-edge contacts can, however, create notches in the test-specimen which would alter the behaviour of the material under test. An alternative method is to attach the extensometer to the shoulders outside the waisted portion of the test-piece (Figure 7.9). Because the cross-sectional area increases rapidly in the short distance from the end of the parallel-sided portion of the test-piece to the clamping position on the shoulder, the amount of extension which will take place in this small portion will be minimal. Provided that the clamping positions are as close as possible to the edges of the shoulders then the measured extension will correspond almost exactly to the extension of the equivalent gauge length, namely the length of the parallel sided portion of the test-piece. With this type of attachment, the extensometer arms can be fastened tightly as there is no risk of adversely affecting the material within the gauge length.

When commencing a creep-test, the test-piece with thermocouples and extensometer attached is raised to the required test temperature before a load is applied. The load should be increased gradually and the extensions

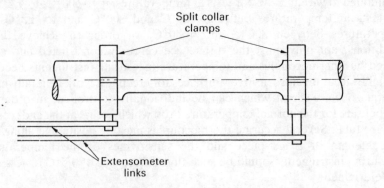

Figure 7.9 Arrangement for shoulder clamping of extensometer on a creep test-piece.

noted for each increment of load, until the nominal stress level for the test is reached. This procedure is necessary in order to determine the relative amounts of elastic and plastic strain on first loading (Figure 7.10).

After the initial plastic deformation due to the application of load has ceased, strain measurements are noted at regular intervals. The time interval between measurements will depend on the creep rate. The general conditions for creep testing are given in BS 3500, Parts 1 and 3 (1969).

7.5 Stress-rupture Testing

When the time to rupture at some particular combination of temperature and stress is required, and there is no need to monitor the progress of creep strain, it is possible to achieve some economy in the use of creep testing machines and test a number of samples simultaneously within the same machine. A series of test-pieces can be mounted in line as a long string within a furnace and the required load applied (Figure 7.11).

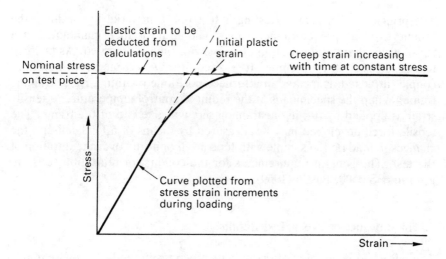

Figure 7.10 Determination of initial plastic strain.

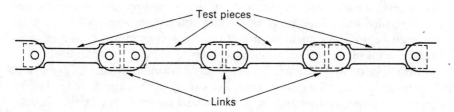

Figure 7.11 String of test-pieces for stress-rupture testing.

As in other forms of creep testing, individual thermo-couples are attached to each specimen and the temperature of test must be controlled within the close limits listed in Section 7.4. When one of the test-pieces breaks, the load on all the remaining specimens will be released. Usually the equipment is arranged so that load release accompanying a fracture will open a microswitch and switch off both the furnace and the clock which records the test duration. The broken test-piece can then be removed and the test continued. It is a requirement of BS 3500 that the time to rupture be measured to an accuracy of ±1 per cent.

The fact that creep testing is a very long-term process means that a creep testing laboratory may need to be equipped with a very large number, possibly running into hundreds, of creep test machines. This is very costly, both in terms of capital equipment cost and the amount of space required. In these circumstances, the economies which can be achieved by testing a string of samples on one machine are worthwhile.

7.6 Relaxation Testing

The principle of relaxation testing is to stress a material by straining the sample to some predetermined value. The strain is then maintained at a constant level and the variation of stress with time is recorded. As in creep testing, close control of temperature is required. A test-piece, with thermo-couples attached, is located in a furnace positioned within a rigid straining frame. When the specimen is at the required control temperature, a tensile strain is applied by turning a straining screw at one end of the frame. The tensile force developed may be measured by means of a load cell and the changes in load on the sample with time are monitored over the duration of the test. The general requirements for the conduct of relaxation tests are given in BS 3500, Part 6 (1969).

7.7 Significance of Creep Test Results

There is a certain amount of scatter with creep results and it is unwise to rely on one test result only for any particular values of stress and temperature. This makes a creep testing programme both very expensive and very lengthy as several results will be needed for each combination of stress and temperature and a wide range of stresses and temperatures will need to be covered before a complete picture of the creep characteristics of a material can be achieved. Even so, with most creep tests being comparatively short term at 1000 or 10 000 hours, it is extremely difficult to predict the behaviour of a material over a long service life. For example, the expected life of steam plant in a power station may be in excess of 20 years (some 200 000 hours).

There is a great deal of uncertainty about extrapolation to predict long term behaviour on the basis of, say, 10 000 hour creep tests.

Another problem is that creep testing determines the behaviour of a material under conditions which involve constancy of stress and temperature whereas, in many practical circumstances, a component may be subject to frequent heating and cooling cycles and variable levels of stress.

The results of creep tests may be used with considerable confidence for design purposes when service conditions involve relatively constant levels of stress and temperature for long periods with a low frequency of heating and cooling cycles. In other cases, considerable care must be exercised in the use of creep data. Often supplementary information is obtained by subjecting prototype materials or components to the conditions expected in service.

7.8 Self Assessment Questions

7.1 Distinguish between primary, secondary and tertiary creep.

7.2 What is meant by the term 'relaxation'?

7.3 What are the main items of information that can be obtained from creep tests?

7.4 Why do directionally solidified alloys and single crystal materials offer advantages for high temperature service?

7.5 In creep testing, why is it considered necessary to have separate thermocouples to record test-piece temperature in addition to those used for the control of furnace temperature?

7.6 In what ways do stress-rupture tests differ from full tensile creep tests?

7.7 A component to operate for long periods at a constant high temperature is designed with an initial length of 150 mm and the maximum increase in length which can be permitted is 2 mm. What will be the maximum value of creep strain rate at the service temperature which can be tolerated if a design life of 15 000 hours is required?

8
Non-destructive Testing

8.1 Introduction

Defects, such as cracks, porosity and inclusions, which may be potentially damaging may be introduced into materials or components during manufacture, and other defects, such as fatigue cracks, may be generated during service. It is necessary to be able to detect and identify such defects and to ascertain their position and size so that decisions can be taken as to whether specific defects can be tolerated or not. A range of non-destructive test (NDT) methods is available for the inspection of materials and components. Some of the features and applications of the main test methods in use are given in Table 8.1. All these NDT systems co-exist and, depending on the application, may either be used singly or in conjunction with one another. There is some overlap between the various test methods but they are complementary to one another. The fact that, for example, ultrasonic testing can reveal both internal and surface flaws does not necessarily mean that it will be the best method for all inspection applications. Much will depend upon the type of flaw present and the shape and size of the components to be examined.

8.2 Visual Inspection

Often the first stage in the examination of a component is visual inspection. Examination by naked eye will only reveal relatively large defects which break the surface but the effectiveness of visual inspection for external surfaces can be improved considerably through use of a hand lens or stereoscopic microscope. Generally, high magnifications are not necessary for this type of inspection. Optical inspection probes, both rigid and flexible, which can be inserted into cavities, ducts and pipes have been developed for the inspection of internal surfaces. An optical inspection probe comprises an

Table 8.1

System	Features	Applicability
Visual inspection probes	Detection of defects which break the surface, surface corrosion, etc	Interior of ducts, pipes and assemblies
Liquid penetrant	Detection of defects which break the surface	Can be used for any metal, many plastics, glass and glazed ceramics
Magnetic particle	Detection of defects which break the surface and sub-surface defects close to the surface	Can only be used for ferro-magnetic materials (most steels and irons)
Electrical methods (Eddy currents)	Detection of surface defects and some sub-surface defects. Can also be used to measure the thickness of non-conductive coatings, e.g. paint on a metal	Can be used for any metal
Ultrasonic testing	Detection of internal defects but can also detect surface flaws	Can be used for most materials
Radiography	Detection of internal defects, surface defects and to check correctness of assemblies	Can be used for most materials but there are limitations on the maximum material thickness

objective lens system at the working end and a viewing eyepiece at the other end, with a fibre optic coherent image guide linking the two (Figure 8.1). Illuminating light is conveyed to the working end of the probe through an optical fibre light guide, and both the optical and illumination systems are contained within either a stainless steel tube, for rigid probes, or a flexible plastic or braided metal sheathing in the case of flexible probes. Inspection probes are made in many sizes with, for rigid probes, diameters ranging from about 2 mm up to about 20 mm. The minimum diameter for flexible probes is about 4 mm. Probe lengths may vary considerably also, and the maximum working length for a 2 mm probe is about 150 mm. The maximum permissible working length increases as probe diameter increases and may be up to 5 m for a 20 mm diameter probe.

Inspection probes can be designed to give either direct viewing ahead of the probe end, or to give a view at some angle to the line of the probe. It is possible to mount a miniature TV camera in place of the normal eyepiece lens system and display an image on a monitor screen.

8.3 Liquid Penetrant Inspection

Liquid penetrant inspection is a technique which can be used to detect defects in a wide range of components, provided that the defect breaks the surface of the material. The principle of the technique is that a liquid is drawn by capillary attraction into the defect and after subsequent development any surface-breaking defects may be rendered visible to the human eye. In order to achieve good defect visibility, the penetrating liquid will either be coloured with a bright and persistent dye or else contain a fluorescent compound. In the former type, the dye is generally red and the developed surface can be viewed in natural or artificial light but in the latter case the component must be viewed under ultraviolet light if indications of defects are to be seen.

Liquid penetrant inspection is an important industrial method and it can be used to indicate the presence of defects such as cracks, laminations, laps and zones of surface porosity in a wide variety of components. The method is applicable to almost any component, whether it be large or small, of simple or complex configuration, and it is employed for the inspection of wrought and cast products in both ferrous and non-ferrous metals and alloys, ceramics, glassware and some polymer components.

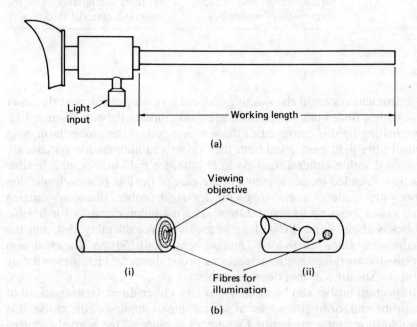

Figure 8.1 (a) Rigid optical inspection probe, (b) Probe ends (i) for direct viewing (ii) for angled viewing.

8.4 Principles of Penetrant Inspection

There are five essential steps in the penetrant inspection method. These are

(a) surface preparation,
(b) application of penetrant,
(c) removal of excess penetrant,
(d) development, and
(e) observation and inspection.

Surface preparation

All surfaces of a component must be thoroughly cleaned and completely dried before the component is subjected to inspection. It is important that any surfaces to be examined for defects must be free from oil, water, grease or other contaminants if successful indication of defects is to be achieved.

Application of penetrant

After surface preparation, liquid penetrant is applied in a suitable manner, so as to form a film of penetrant over the component surface. In practice, penetrants may be applied to the surface of the component using one of several methods. The method chosen will depend on the size, shape and the number of parts to be inspected. It will also depend on whether or not components are to be examined *in situ*. When large numbers of comparatively small parts are to be examined, total immersion of the components in a tank containing liquid penetrant is preferred. When it is only required to examine individual components or to inspect components *in situ*, the penetrant can be applied by brush, from a low pressure spray, or from an aerosol spray can. The length of time that the penetrant is in contact with the component is important. Penetrant will seep into fairly large flaws in a few seconds but it may take up to 30 minutes for the liquid to penetrate into very small defects and tight cracks.

Removal of excess penetrant

It is now necessary to remove excess penetrant from the surface of the component. Some penetrants can be washed off the surface with water, whilst others require the use of specific solvents. Uniform removal of excess penetrant is necessary for effective inspection.

Development

The development stage is necessary to reveal clearly the presence of any defect. The developer is usually a very fine chalk powder. This may be applied dry, but more commonly is applied by spraying the surface with chalk dust suspended in a volatile carrier fluid. A thin uniform layer of chalk is deposited on the surface of the component. Penetrant liquid present within defects will be slowly drawn by capillary action into the pores of the chalk. There will be some spread of penetrant within the developer and this will magnify the apparent width of a defect. When a dye penetrant is used, the dye colour must be in sharp contrast to the uniform white of the chalk covered surface. The development stage may sometimes be omitted when a fluorescent penetrant is used. If it takes a long time for penetrant to be drawn into a tight crack then it follows that a similar length of time will be needed for liquid to be drawn from the defect by the developer. In consequence, development times of between 10 and 30 minutes are generally required to ensure that all defect indications are visible.

Observation and inspection

After an optimum developing time has been allowed, the component surface is inspected for indications of penetrant 'bleedback' into the developer. Dye-penetrant inspection is carried out in strong lighting conditions, whilst fluorescent-penetrant inspection is performed in a suitable screened area using ultraviolet light. The latter technique causes the penetrant to emit visible light, and defects are brilliantly outlined. The five essential operations are shown in Figure 8.2.

8.5 Advantages, Limitations and Applications of Penetrant Inspection

The liquid penetrant process is comparatively simple as no electronic systems are involved, and the equipment necessary is cheaper than that required for other non-destructive testing systems. The obvious major limitation of liquid penetrant systems is that it can detect surface-breaking defects only.

Sub-surface defects require additional inspection methods. Other factors inhibiting the effectiveness of liquid penetrant inspection are surface roughness, and porous materials. The latter, in particular, can produce false indications, since each pore will register as a potential defect.

The range of applications of liquid penetrant testing is extremely wide and varied. The system is used in the aerospace industries by both producers for the quality control of production and by users during regular maintenance and safety checks. Typical components which are checked by this system are turbine rotor discs and blades, aircraft wheels, castings, forged components and welded assemblies. Many automotive parts, particularly aluminium castings and forgings, including pistons and cylinder heads, are subjected to this form of quality control inspection before assembly. Penetrant testing is also used for the regular in-service examination of the bogie frames of railway locomotives and rolling stock in the search for fatigue cracking. Figure 8.3 shows the inspection of the inlet assembly of an aircraft engine. The operator is looking for surface cracks under ultraviolet light, after the assembly has been processed with fluorescent penetrant. In general manufacturing industry, the techniques are widely used for the process and quality control checking of castings, forgings and weldments.

8.6 Magnetic Particle Inspection

Magnetic particle inspection is a sensitive method of locating surface and some sub-surface defects in ferromagnetic components. The basic processing parameters depend on relatively simple concepts. In essence, when a

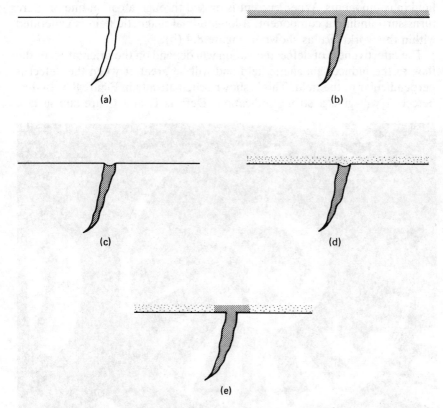

Figure 8.2 Stages in penetrant testing: (a) material surface clean and grease-free; (b) penetrant absorbed into defect; (c) excess penetrant removed, but liquid remains in defect; (d) developer applied to surface; (e) penetrant absorbed into developer giving indication of defect.

ferromagnetic component is magnetised, magnetic discontinuities that lie in a direction approximately perpendicular to the field direction will result in the formation of a strong 'leakage field'. This leakage field is present at and above the surface of the magnetised component, and its presence can be detected by the utilisation of finely divided magnetic particles. The application of dry particles or wet particles in a liquid carrier, over the surface of the component, results in a collection of magnetic particles at a discontinuity. The 'magnetic bridge' so formed indicates the location, size, and shape of the discontinuity.

Current passing through any straight conductor such as a wire or bar creates a circular magnetic field around the conductor. When the conductor is a ferromagnetic material, the current induces a magnetic field within the conductor as well as within the surrounding space. Hence, a component magnetised in this manner is circularly magnetised, as shown in Figure 8.4 (a). An electric current can also be used to create a longitudinal magnetic field in components. When current is passed through a coil of one or more turns surrounding a component, a longitudinal magnetic field is generated within the workpiece as shown in Figure 8.4 (b).

The effectiveness of defect indication will depend on the orientation of the flaw to the induced magnetic field and will be greatest when the defect is perpendicular to the field. This is shown schematically in Figure 8.5. In this, defect A will give a strong indication. Defects B and C are sub-surface

Figure 8.3 Inspection of inlet assembly of aircraft gas turbine using ultra-violet light after application of fluorescent penetrant. (Courtesy of Magnaflux Ltd.)

defects. An indication will be obtained in respect of defect B as it is normal to the magnetic field but defect C will not be indicated. In the case of defect C, it is too deep within the material to give an indication but, even if such a defect were close to the surface, its alignment with the magnetic field would render detection unlikely.

Generally, in order to indicate the presence of all flaws, a component will need to be magnetised more than once. For components of relatively simple shape, this is achieved by, firstly, inducing circular magnetisation to indicate longitudinal defects. The component is then demagnetised before magnetising for a second time within a coil to induce longitudinal magnetisation which will enable transverse defects to be located.

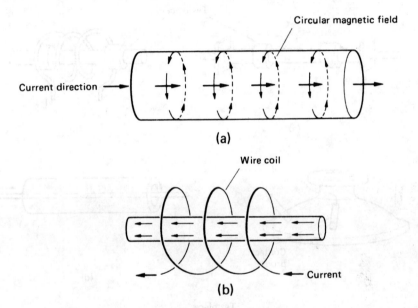

Figure 8.4 (a) Current passes through workpiece including circular magnetisation, (b) Longitudinal magnetisation induced by placing workpiece within a coil.

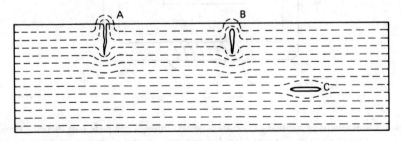

Figure 8.5 Magnetic flaw detection: detectable surface leakage fields produced by defects A and B. Defect C is likely to remain undetected.

8.7 Magnetisation Methods

Magnetisation of a component could be accomplished using permanent magnets but generally magnetic fields are induced by passing a heavy current through the component, by placing a coil around or close to the component under test, or by making the component part of a magnetic circuit, for example by means of a hand yoke. These basic magnetisation principles are shown in Figure 8.6. The actual method used will depend on the size, shape and complexity of the parts to be inspected and, for components to be inspected *in situ*, the accessibility to such components.

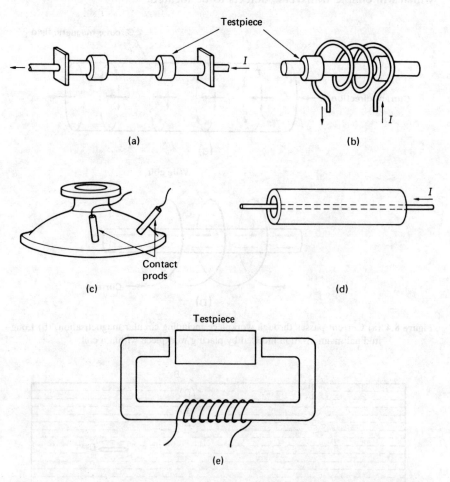

Figure 8.6 Magnetising methods: (a) current passed through complete part inducing circular magnetisation; (b) part placed within coil inducing longitudinal magnetisation; (c) prod contacts placed on surface of large casting; (d) hollow section magnetised by threading a conducting cable through it; (e) part magnetised within magnetic yoke.

Direct electrical contact at each end of a component, so that current passes through the whole part (Figure 8.6 (a)), is a rapid and reliable method which is very suitable for the inspection of relatively small components. Small to medium size components in which one dimension, namely length, predominates can be readily magnetised in a longitudinal direction by placing within a coil. (Figure 8.6 (b)). This technique is particularly useful for the location of transverse flaws in such items as axles, crankshafts and camshafts. Flexible cables with prod contact ends are widely used for the inspection of large castings and forgings. A component with a continuous hole through it can be magnetised by energising a straight conducting cable passing through the hole (Figure 8.6 (d)). This inspection technique is often used in the examination of parts such as pipe connectors, hollow cylinders, gear wheels and large nuts. For certain types of application, an electro-magnetic yoke may be used (Figure 8.6 (e)). This technique is suitable for the examination of a variety of shapes. One example of this method is the search for forging laps and other surface defects in crane hooks.

The magnetic particles which are used for inspection may be made from any ferromagnetic material of low remanence and they are usually finely divided powders of either metal oxides or metals. The particles are classified as *dry* or *wet*. Dry particles are carried in air or gas suspension while wet particles are carried in liquid suspension. Very high sensitivities are possible with wet particle inspection, particularly when a fluorescent chemical is adsorbed on the particles and inspection is made under ultraviolet light. In the best conditions, it is possible to detect cracks with a width of as little as 10^{-3} mm.

8.8 Advantages, Limitations and Applications of Magnetic Particle Inspection

Magnetic particle inspection is a sensitive means of detecting very fine surface flaws. It is also possible to obtain indications from some discontinuities that do not break through the surface provided that they are close to the surface. The major limitations of the technique are that it is only suitable for ferromagnetic materials, that for the best results the induced magnetic field should be normal to any defect and thus two or more magnetising sequences will be necessary, and a demagnetising procedure will need to be carried out for many components after inspection. The sensitivity of magnetic particle inspection is very good generally, but this will be reduced if the surface of the component is covered by a film of paint or other non-magnetic layer.

The principal industrial uses of magnetic particle inspection are for in-process inspection, final inspection and the inspection of components as part of planned maintenance and overhaul schedules. The methods are well suited to the inspection of castings and forgings and components such as crankshafts, connecting rods, flywheels, crane hooks, axles and shafts.

8.9 Electrical Test Methods

The basic principle underlying the electrical test methods is that electrical eddy currents and/or magnetic effects are induced within the material or component under test and, from an assessment of the effects, deductions can be made about the nature and condition of the test-piece. These techniques are highly versatile and, with the appropriate equipment and test method, can be used to detect surface and sub-surface defects within components, determine the thickness of surface coatings, provide information about structural features such as crystal grain size and heat treatment condition, and also to measure physical properties including electrical conductivity, magnetic permeability and physical hardness.

If a coil carrying an alternating current is placed in proximity to a conductive material, secondary or eddy currents will be induced within the material. The induced currents will produce a magnetic field surrounding the coil. This interaction between fields causes a back e.m.f. in the coil and, hence, a change in the coil impedance value. If a material is uniform in composition and dimensions, the impedance value of a search coil placed close to the surface should be the same at all points on the surface, apart from some variation observed close to the edges of the sample. If the material contains a discontinuity, the distribution of eddy currents, and their magnitude, will be altered in its vicinity and there will be a consequent reduction in the magnetic field associated with the eddy currents, so altering the coil impedance value.

Eddy currents flow in closed loops within a material and both the magnitude and the timing or phase of the currents will depend on a number of factors. These factors include the magnitude of the magnetic field surrounding the primary coil, the electrical and magnetic properties of the material and the presence or otherwise of discontinuities or dimensional changes within the material. Several types of search coil are used, two common types being the flat or pancake type coil which is suitable for the examination of flat surfaces and the solenoid type coil which can be used in conjunction with solid or tubular cylindrical parts. For tubes, a solenoid type coil may be placed around the tube or inserted into the bore. The patterns of eddy currents obtained with these coil types is shown in Figure 8.7.

If a component contains a crack or other discontinuity, the flow pattern of eddy currents will be altered and this will cause a change in the magnetic field and, hence, a change in coil impedance. A schematic representation of the effect of a discontinuity on eddy current pattern is shown in Figure 8.8. The impedance of a coil can be determined by measuring the voltage across it. In eddy current test equipment, changes in coil impedance can be indicated on a meter or a chart recorder or displayed on the screen of a cathode ray tube.

At component edges, eddy current flow is distorted, because the eddy currents are unable to flow beyond this limiting barrier. The magnitude of

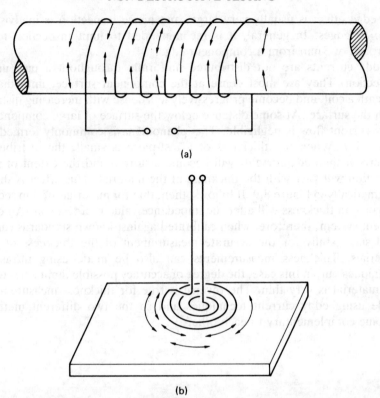

(a)

(b)

Figure 8.7 (a) Solenoid type coil around bar producing circumferential eddy currents, (b) Pancake type coil producing circular eddy currents within flat plate.

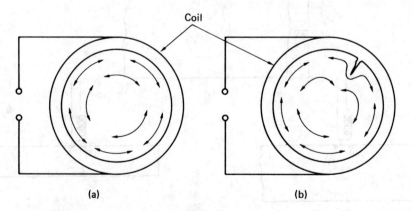

Coil

(a)   (b)

Figure 8.8 Cross-section of a bar within a solenoid type coil showing eddy current pattern; (a) defect free section – uniform eddy currents; (b) eddy current pattern distorted by the presence of a defect.

this edge effect is usually very large, and hence inspection is inadvisable close to edges. In general, it is recommended to limit inspection to an approach of 3 mm from a component edge.

Eddy currents are not distributed uniformly throughout a part under inspection. They are most dense at the component surface, immediately beneath a coil, and become progressively less dense with increasing distance from the surface. At some distance below the surface of large components, eddy current flow is negligible. This phenomena is commonly termed the *skin effect*. When the thickness of a test-piece is small, the distribution pattern of the eddy currents will become distorted and the extent of such distortion will vary with the thickness of the material. This effect is shown schematically in Figure 8.9. It follows, then, that for materials of thin section a change in thickness will alter the impedance value of a test coil. An eddy current system, therefore, when calibrated against known standards can be used successfully for the accurate measurement of the thickness of thin materials. Thickness measurements can also be made using ultrasonic techniques but, in this case, the degree of accuracy possible diminishes when the material is very thin. The reverse is true for thickness measurements made using eddy current techniques and so the two different methods become complementary to each other.

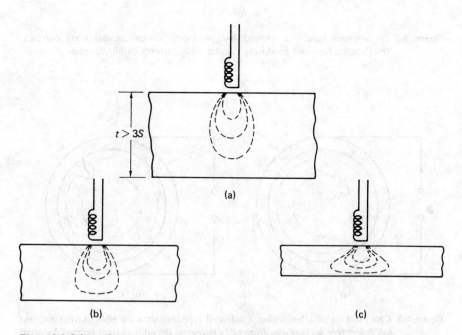

Figure 8.9 Schematic representation of distortion of eddy current distribution in thin sections.

8.10 Inspection Frequency and Coil Types

The inspection frequencies used in electrical techniques range from 20 Hz to 10 MHz. Inspection of non-magnetic materials is performed at frequencies within the range 1 kHz – MHz, whilst frequencies lower than 1 kHz are often employed with magnetic materials. Usually, the actual frequency used in any specific test is a compromise in order to attain optimum sensitivity at the desired penetration depth. For non-magnetic materials, the choice becomes relatively simple when it is required to detect surface flaws only. Frequencies as high as possible (several MHz) are used. However, detection of sub-surface flaws at a considerable depth demand low frequencies, sacrificing sensitivity. Hence, small flaws may not be detected under such conditions. Inspection of ferromagnetic materials demands very low frequencies because of the relatively low penetration depth in these materials. Higher frequencies can be used to inspect for surface conditions only. However, even the higher frequencies used in these applications are still considerably lower than those used to inspect non-magnetic materials for similar conditions.

There are several different coil arrangements which can be used in eddy current testing and some of the more common types are shown in Figure 8.10. A single primary solenoid type coil may be used for the routine inspection of cylindrical bars or tubes. The test-piece is passed through the coil (Figure 8.10(a)). Variations in coil impedance value as the test-piece moves through the coil will indicate the presence of flaws. When it is not possible to place a coil around the outside of a tube as, for example, during the routine *in situ* inspection of heat exchanger or condenser tubes the coil can be wound on a bobbin and inserted into the bore of the tubes.

Frequently, a double primary coil system is used in tube inspection (Figure 8.10 (b)). The two coils are identical and are connected to adjacent arms of an electrical bridge network. When the tube is uniform, the bridge circuit will be balanced but if one coil is in proximity to a crack, or an area where corrosion has caused a thinning of the tube wall, the bridge will be thrown out of balance.

The differential coil system (Figure 8.10(c)) is sometimes used instead of the double primary coil for tube and bar inspection. When the material is uniform there will be zero voltage across AB but, if a flaw existed at some point X in the specimen, a voltage would exist between AB. One of the most widely-used arrangements is the surface coil (Figure 8.10(d)) in which a coil is wound around a ferrite core. The coil is held normal to the surface of the material being inspected. The ferrite core will concentrate the magnetic flux and increase the sensitivity for the detection of small defects.

8.11 Phase Analysis

One method of representing the signals from eddy current inspection probes is by the phasor technique or phase analysis. There is a phase difference between the reactive and resistive components of the measurement voltage. Consider the voltages as vectors A and B. The frequency is the same for

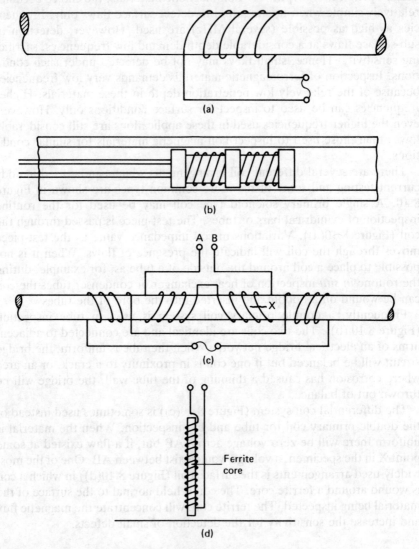

Figure 8.10 Coil arrangements: (a) single primary coil around bar; (b) twin coil bobbin inside tube; (c) differential coil system; (d) surface coil with ferrite core.

both and, therefore, the radian velocity ($\omega = 2\pi f$). The equations describing the vectors will be of the form: $\sin (\omega t + \varphi)$ where φ is the phase angle.

The resistive and reactive components of a measurement (probe coil) voltage can be fed to the 'X' plates and 'Y' plates respectively of a cathode ray oscilloscope and displayed as a two-dimensional representation. There are several ways in which impedance data can be displayed on the screen of a cathode ray oscilloscope.

One method is the *vector point* method. In this method, a spot is projected onto the screen representing the impedance of the coil in air. When the probe coil is placed in contact with a test specimen, the spot will move to correspond with the impedance change. The position of the spot for a reference test-block can be adjusted to be at the centre of the screen. Any variation or anomaly in the component under test will cause a movement of the spot and the direction of this movement will indicate the cause of the variation. When more than one variable is present, they can often be isolated by vector analysis (Figure 8.11). A storage-type oscilloscope is used with eddy current test equipment. The impedance changes caused by various types of defect or by changes in conductivity will give screen displays as in Figures 8.11 (a) and (b).

8.12 Advantages, Limitations and Applications of Electrical Methods

The electrical eddy current system is a highly versatile system which can be used to detect not only cracks, but several other conditions, including corrosion. The test equipment may be small and portable and, with a suitable selection of test probes, can be used in many situations. However, the correct interpretation of signal indications does require considerable skill and experience on the part of the operator. The eddy current equipment which is used for the quality control inspection of the products of many material manufacturing processes is often completely automatic and is

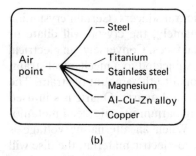

(b)

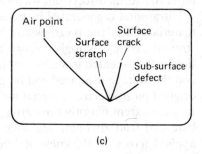

(c)

Figure 8.11 (a) Impedance plane display on oscilloscope showing differing conductivities. (b) Impedance plane display showing defect indications.

highly sophisticated. Production of tubing, bar stock and wire are checked in this way by many manufacturers. The range of applications in which eddy current inspection is used successfully is almost infinite. Some typical uses are the routine in-service inspection of many components in aircraft, including undercarriage wheels, routine inspection of railway track, accurate determination of thickness, including wall-thinning due to corrosion and measurement of the thickness of surface coatings on metals. The ability to determine the conductivity of metals by means of phase analysis is utilised in several ways, including the identification and sorting of materials and detecting areas of heat-damaged skin on aircraft structures. Overheated areas, which could suffer a major loss of strength, show an increased electrical conductivity value.

8.13 Ultrasonic Testing

Ultrasonic techniques are very widely used for the detection of internal defects in materials, but they can also be used for the detection of small surface cracks. Ultrasonics are used for the quality control inspection of part processed material, such as rolled slabs, as well as for the inspection of finished components. The techniques are also in regular use for the in-service testing of parts and assemblies.

Sound waves are elastic waves which can be transmitted through both fluid and solid media. The audible range of frequency is from about 20 Hz to about 20 kHz but it is possible to produce elastic waves of the same nature as sound at frequencies up to 500 MHz. Elastic waves with frequencies higher than the audio range are described as ultrasonic. The waves used for the non-destructive inspection of materials are usually within the frequency range 0.5 MHz to 20 MHz. In fluids, sound waves are of the longitudinal compression type in which particle displacement is in the direction of wave propagation but in solids shear waves, with particle displacement normal to the direction of wave travel, and elastic surface waves, can also occur. These latter are termed Rayleigh waves.

Ultrasound is generated by piezo-electric transducers. Certain crystalline materials show the piezo-electric effect, namely, the crystal will dilate or strain if a voltage is applied across the crystal faces. Conversely, an electrical field will be created in such a crystal if it is subjected to a mechanical strain, and the voltage produced will be proportional to the amount of strain. The original piezo-electric material used was natural quartz. Quartz is still used to some extent but other materials including barium titanate, lead metanio-bate and lead zirconate are used widely. When an alternating voltage is applied across the thickness of a disc of piezo-electric material, the disc will contract and expand and in so doing will generate a compression wave normal to the disc in the surrounding medium. A transducer for sound generation will also detect sound. An ultrasonic wave incident on a crystal will cause it to vibrate, producing an alternating current across the crystal faces. In some ultrasonic testing techniques, two transducers are used, one to transmit the beam and the other acting as the receiver, but in very many cases only one transducer is necessary. This acts as both transmitter and receiver. Ultrasound is transmitted as a series of pulses of extremely short duration and during the time interval between transmissions the crystal can detect reflected signals.

When a beam of longitudinal compression sound waves reaches a boundary between two media, a proportion of the incident waves will be reflected at the interface and a proportion will be transmitted across the interface. At an air/metal interface, reflection of sound waves will be almost 100 per cent. A fluid, oil or water, is needed as a couplant between an ultrasound transmitter and metal to permit some of the sound energy to be transmitted across the interface into the metal. For normal incidence waves, the transmission across the interface will be of the compression wave type. When the incident beam is at some angle other than normal that portion of the beam which is transmitted across the interface will be refracted. However, there may be two refracted beams transmitted into the metal because part of the transmitted energy is converted into the shear wave mode. One refracted beam will be of the compression type while the other will be a shear wave, as shown in Figure 8.12.

In ultrasonic inspection, the presence of two types of wave with differing velocities within the material would give confusing results and so the angle of incidence is adjusted to be greater than the critical angle for compression wave refraction. This critical angle for total reflection of an incident compression wave at a perspex/steel interface is 27.5°. Angle probes for shear wave propagation (see Section 8.14) are generally available with angles of 35°, 45°, 60°, 70° and 80°, all angles being measured from the normal.

If it is required to generate a surface, or Rayleigh, wave the angle of incidence should be adjusted to a second critical angle to produce a Rayleigh wave at a refracted angle of 90°. The value of this critical angle for a perspex/steel interface is 57°.

An ultrasonic beam being transmitted through a metal will be totally reflected at the far surface of the material, a metal/air interface. It will also be wholly or partially reflected by any internal surface, namely cracks or laminations, porosity and non-metallic inclusions, subject to the limitation that the size of the object is not less than one wave length. From this it follows that the sensitivity and defect resolution will increase as the frequency of the beam is increased.

Some metallic materials can only be inspected satisfactorily with a relatively low frequency sound beam because the use of high frequencies could cause a mass of reflections from a normal structural constituent which would mask the indications from defects. This situation arises in the inspection of grey cast iron components where the flakes or nodules of graphite in the iron structure may have a size of several millimetres.

8.14 Ultrasonic Probes

There are several types of transmitter probes in use but each type consists of a crystal which is placed in contact, either directly or through a protective cover, with the material under test. A step voltage, of short duration, is applied to the crystal and this causes the crystal to vibrate at its natural frequency. After the step voltage has been removed, the crystal oscillation is required to die as soon as possible, and the crystal is usually backed by a damping material to assist this process. Probes may be of the normal type, or be angled.

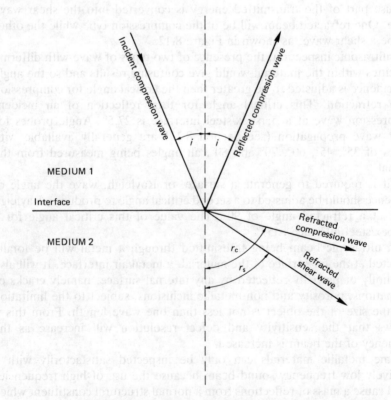

Figure 8.12 Reflection and refraction at an interface.

Normal probes

A normal probe is designed to transmit a compression wave into the test material at right angles to the material surface. In some cases the crystal surface is uncovered so that it may be placed directly, via an oil or water film, in contact with the test material. Alternatively, the crystal may be protected by a layer of metal, ceramic or perspex. In the last case, the perspex block may be shaped to allow for normal transmission into material with a curved surface (Figure 8.13 (a)).

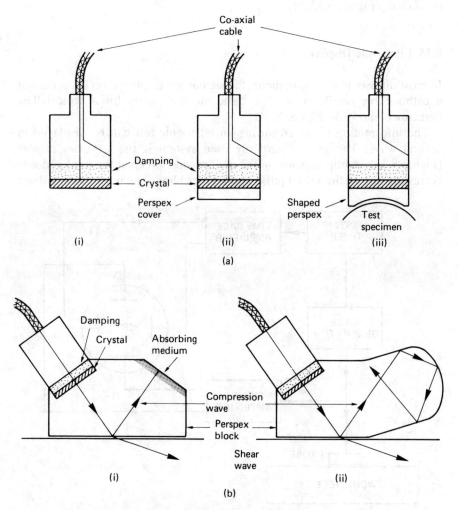

Figure 8.13 Probe construction: (a) normal probes, (i) uncovered probe, (ii) covered probe, (iii) normal probe for curved surface; (b) Angle probes, (i) with sound absorbent, (ii) shaped for reflected wave dissipation.

Angle probes

Angle probes are designed to transmit shear waves or Rayleigh waves into the test material. The general construction of an angle probe is similar to that of a normal probe with the crystal embedded in a shaped perspex block. There is a reflected compression wave produced at the perspex/metal interface. This reflected wave could possibly return to the crystal and give confusing signals. To obviate this, an absorbent medium, such as rubber, is built into the probe. An alternative method is to shape the perspex block in such a way that the reflected wave is 'bounced' around several times until its energy is dissipated. This is possible since perspex has a high absorption coefficient (Figure 8.13(b)).

8.15 Ultrasonic Display

In most ultrasonic test equipment, the signals are displayed on the screen of a cathode ray oscilloscope. The basic block diagram for a typical flaw detector is shown in Figure 8.14.

The information obtained during an ultrasonic test can be displayed in several ways. The most commonly used system is the *'A' scan display* (Figure 8.15). A blip appears on the oscilloscope screen at the left hand side corresponding to the initial pulse and further blips appear on the time base

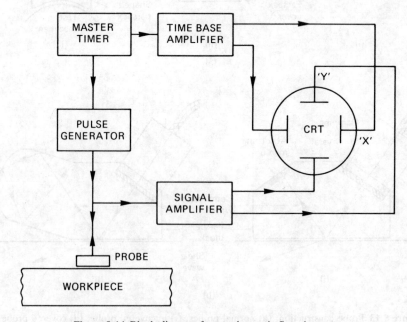

Figure 8.14 Block diagram for an ultrasonic flaw detector.

corresponding to any signal echoes received. The height of the echo is generally proportional to the size of the reflecting surface but it is affected by the distance travelled by the signal and attenuation effects within the material. The linear position of the echo is proportional to the distance of the reflecting surface from the probe, assuming a linear timebase. This is the normal type of display for hand probe inspection techniques.

8.16 Techniques for Defect Detection

The presence of a defect within a material may be found using ultrasonics with either a transmission technique or a reflection technique.

Normal probe reflection method

This is the most commonly used technique in ultrasonic testing, and is illustrated in Figure 8.15. The pulse is wholly or partially reflected by any defect in the material and received by the single probe, which combines as transmitter and receiver. The time interval between transmission of pulse and reception of echo is used to indicate the distance of the defect from the probe.

Angle probe transmission method

There are certain testing situations in which it is not possible to place a normal probe at right angles to a defect and the only reasonable solution is offered by angle probes. A good example of this technique is in the inspection of butt welds in parallel sided plate. The transmitter and receiver probes are arranged as in Figure 8.16(a).

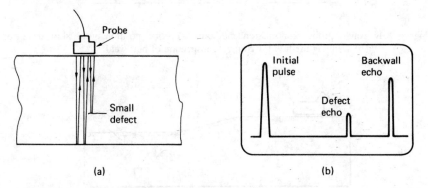

(a)   (b)

Figure 8.15 'A' scan display: (a) reflections obtained from defect and back wall; (b) representation of 'A' scan screen display.

If there is any defect in the weld zone this will cause a reduction in the received signal strength. Distance AB is known as the skip distance and, for the complete scanning of a weld, the probes should be moved over the plate surface as shown in Figure 8.16 (b). In practice, both probes would be mounted in a jig so that they are always at the correct separation distance.

Inspection using a surface wave probe

A Rayleigh, or surface, wave can be used for the detection of surface cracks (Figure 8.17). The presence of a surface defect will reflect the surface wave to give an echo signal in the usual way. Surface waves will follow the surface contours and so the method is suitable for shaped components such as turbine blades.

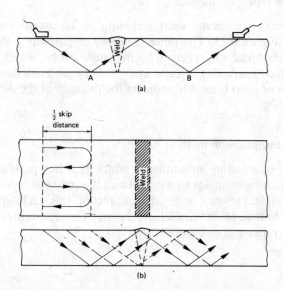

Figure 8.16 Angle probe transmission method: (a) probe positions and skip distance; (b) scanning method for complete inspection of butt weld.

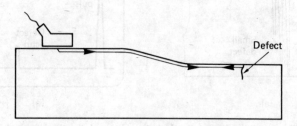

Figure 8.17 Crack detection using a surface wave probe.

8.17 Applications of Ultrasonic Testing

As has been seen in the foregoing paragraphs, ultrasonic test methods are suitable for the detection, identification and size assessment of a wide variety of both surface and sub-surface defects in materials, provided that there is, for the reflection technique, access to one surface. Using hand-held probes, many types of component can be tested, including *in situ* testing. This latter capability makes the method particularly attractive for the routine inspection of aircraft and road and rail vehicles in the search for incipient fatigue cracks. In aircraft inspection, specific test methods have been developed for each particular application and the procedures listed in the appropriate manuals must be followed if consistent results are to be achieved. In many cases, a probe will be specially designed for one specific type of inspection. There are automated systems also which are highly suitable for the routine inspection of production items at both an intermediate stage and the final stage of manufacture.

Present day ultrasonic equipment is compact and light and will operate from either a standard mains supply or from its internal battery. A typical set would have dimensions of about 300 mm × 250 mm × 100 mm and weigh less than 5 kg. The equipment is extremely portable, relatively inexpensive and extremely versatile, and this has helped ultrasonic testing to become an indispensable tool for those concerned with all aspects of quality control and quality assurance.

8.18 Principles of Radiography

Very short wavelength electromagnetic radiation, namely X or γ-rays will penetrate through solid media but will be partially absorbed by the medium. The amount of absorption which will occur will depend upon the density and thickness of the material the radiation is passing through and also upon the characteristics of the radiation. The radiation which passes through the material can be detected and recorded on either film or sensitised paper, viewed on a fluorescent screen or detected and monitored by electronic sensing equipment. Strictly speaking, the term *radiography* implies a process in which an image is produced on film.

The basic principle of radiographic inspection is that the object to be examined is placed in the path of a beam of radiation from an X-ray or γ-ray source. A recording medium, usually film is placed close to the object being examined but on the opposite side from the beam source (as shown in Figure 8.18). X or γ-radiation cannot be focussed as visible light can be focussed and, in many instances, the radiation will come from the source as a conical beam. Some of the radiation will be absorbed by the object but some will travel through the object and impinge on the film producing a latent image.

If the object contains a flaw which has a different absorptive power from that of the object material, the amount of radiation emerging from the object directly beneath the flaw will differ from that emerging from adjacent flaw-free regions. When the film has been developed, there will be an area of different image density which corresponds to the flaw in the material. Thus the flaw will be seen as a shadow within the developed radiograph. This shadow may be of lesser or greater density than the surrounding image depending on the nature of the defect and its relative absorptive characteristics.

8.19 X-rays and γ-rays

The very high frequency (short wavelength) radiation known as X-rays and γ-rays is the only form of electromagnetic radiation which will penetrate solid and opaque material. X-rays and γ-rays are indistinguishable from one another. The only difference between them is the manner of their formation. X-rays are formed by bombarding a metal target material with a stream of high velocity electrons within an X-ray tube. γ-rays, on the other hand, are emitted as part of the decay process of radioactive substances.

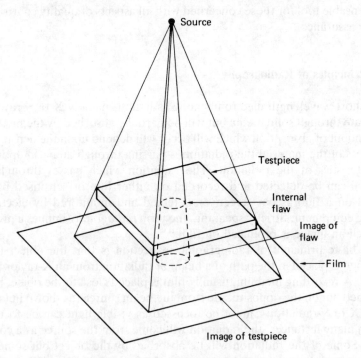

Figure 8.18 Schematic diagram showing a radiographic system.

The major components of an X-ray tube are a cathode to emit electrons and an anode target, both being contained within an evacuated tube or envelope. The general arrangement is shown in Figure 8.19. The cathode is a filament coil of tungsten wire. An electric current at a low voltage flows through the cathode filament to heat it to incandescence and stimulate the thermionic emission of electrons. A large electrical potential difference (the tube voltage) exists between the cathode and anode target to accelerate the electrons across the space separating the two. X-ray tube voltages generally range from 50 kV to 1 MV.

A focussing cup or focussing coil is placed close to the cathode. This acts as an electromagnetic lens to focus the thermionic emission into a fine beam aimed at the centre of the anode target material. The anode comprises a small piece of the target metal, which is usually tungsten, embedded in a mass of copper. Tungsten is used as a target material because it is an efficient emitter of X-rays and because it possesses an extremely high melting point, 3380 °C, and can therefore withstand the high temperatures generated by the impinging electrons. Only a small amount of the incident electron beam energy is converted into X-ray energy, the remainder being emitted as heat energy. For this reason, the tungsten target material is embedded in a copper block which is water-cooled or oil-cooled so that the heat energy generated can be readily dissipated by conduction through the copper.

The X-ray tube envelope may be made of glass, a ceramic material such as alumina, a metal, or a combination of materials. The majority of X-ray tubes made these days are of ceramic/metal construction and these can be made smaller, for any particular tube voltage rating, than glass/metal tubes. The tube envelope must possess good structural strength at high temperatures in

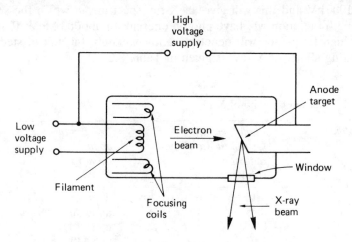

Figure 8.19 Schematic view of an X-ray tube.

order to withstand the combined effects of radiated heat from the anode and the forces exerted by atmospheric pressure on the evacuated chamber. The shape of the envelope may vary with the tube voltage rating and the nature of the anode and cathode design. The envelope must contain a window opposite the anode to permit the X-ray beam to leave the tube. The window is made of a low atomic number element to minimise X-ray absorption. A 3–4 mm thickness of beryllium is generally used as a window material. The electrical connections for anode and cathode are fused into the walls of the envelope. The X-ray tube is contained within a metal housing which is well insulated to give protection from high-voltage electrical shock and this housing usually possesses a high-voltage plug and socket which will permit the rapid disconnection of the electrical cables which connect the tube to the high voltage generator unit. The portable X-ray units which are used for on-site work are generally self contained with both the high voltage generator and the X-ray tube contained within the same housing. In this case, there are no high voltage cables outside the unit.

There are three important variables in X-ray tubes. These are the filament current, the tube voltage and the tube current. A change in the filament current will alter the temperature of the filament which will change the rate of thermionic emission of electrons. An increase in the tube voltage, the potential difference between cathode and anode, will increase the energy of the electron beam and, hence, will increase the energy and penetrating power of the X-ray beam which is produced. The third variable, the tube current, is the magnitude of the electron flow between cathode and anode and is directly related to the filament temperature. (The tube current is usually referred to as the milli-amperage of the tube.) The intensity of the X-ray beam produced by the tube is approximately proportional to the tube milli-amperage. The upper practical limit for the voltage of an X-ray tube is about 1000 kV and this will give an X-ray spectrum in which the shortest wavelength radiation will have photon energies of about 1 MeV. Radiation of this high frequency will penetrate approximately 140 mm of steel. The penetrating ability of X-rays is given in Table 8.2.

Table 8.2 Penetration ability of X-rays

Tube voltage (kV)	Photon energy for lowest wavelength radiation (MeV)	Penetration ability (mm of steel)
150	0.15	up to 25
250	0.25	up to 70
400	0.4	up to 100
1000	1.0	5 to 140

γ-radiation is emitted during the decay of radioactive nuclei. Unlike the broad 'white' spectrum of radiation obtained from an X-ray tube, a γ-ray emitter will give one or more discrete radiation wave-lengths, each one with is own characteristic photon energy. Radium, a naturally occurring radioactive element has been used as a source of γ-radiation for radiography but it is far more usual to use radio-isotopes produced in a nuclear reactor.

The specific isotopes which are generally used as γ-ray sources for radiography are caesium 137, cobalt 60, iridium 192 and thulium 170. (The numbers are the atomic mass numbers of the radioactive nuclei). There is a continuous reduction in the intensity of radiation emitted from a γ-ray source as more and more unstable nuclei decay. The rate of decay decreases exponentially with time according to

$$I_t = I_0 \, e^{-kt}$$

where I_0 is the initial intensity, I_t is the intensity of radiation at time t and k is a constant for a particular disintegrating atomic species. An important characteristic of each particular radio-isotope is its *half-life* period. This is the time taken for the intensity of the emitted radiation to fall to one-half of its original value. After two half-life time intervals, the intensity will fall to ¼ of the original value, after three half-life time intervals, the intensity will fall to ⅛ of the original value, and so on. Another characteristic of a γ-ray source is the source strength. The source strength is the number of atomic disintegrations per second and is measured in curies (one curie is 3.7×10^{10} disintegrations per second). The source strength decreases exponentially with time, and the source strength at any given time can be determined using the expression

$$S_t = S_0 \, e^{-kt}$$

The radiation intensity, usually measured in roentgens per hour at one metre (rhm) is given by source strength (in curies) × radiation output (rhm per curie). (One roentgen is the amount of radiation that will produce ions carrying one electrostatic unit of energy in 1.293 mg of air). The value of radiation output is a constant for any particular isotope. Another term used in connection with γ-ray sources is *specific activity*. This characteristic, expressed in curies per gramme, is a measure of the degree of concentration of the source.

The characteristics of the commonly used γ-sources for radiography are given in Table 8.3. Commercial radioactive sources are usually metallic in nature, but may be chemical salts or gases adsorbed on carbon. The source is encapsulated in a thin protective covering. This may be a thin sheath of stainless steel or aluminium. By containing the radioactive material in a capsule of this type it prevents spillage or leakage of the material and reduces the possibility of accidental mishandling. The encapsulated source is housed in a lead-lined steel container.

Table 8.3 Characteristics of γ-ray sources

Source isotope	Half-life period	Photon energy (MeV)	Radiation output (rhm/curie)	Effective penetrating power (mm of steel)
Caesium-137	33 years	0.66	0.39	75
Cobalt-60	5.3 years	1.17, 1.33	1.35	225
Iridium-192	74 days	12 rays from 0.13 to 0.61	0.55	75
Thulium-170	128 days	0.084	0.0045	12 (aluminium not steel)

8.20 Obtaining and Assessing a Radiograph

The obtaining of satisfactory radiographs requires a very high degree of skill and expertise on the part of the radiographer as there are very many factors which affect the formation of an X-ray or γ-ray image. When it is desired to radiograph some object or component, the composition, density and dimensions of the object will largely determine the quality of the radiation which will be used. The source must produce radiation which will be sufficiently penetrating for the type and thickness of material to be inspected and so X-ray tube voltage or type of γ-radiation source will be selected accordingly. The selection of a particular grade of radiographic film will be made on the basis of its sensitivity to the variations of radiation intensity which are expected after transmission through the object. However, the amount of radiation expected to reach the film will be affected by several other factors, including the intensity of the incident radiation (governed by the X-ray tube current or the strength of a gamma source in curies), the source-to-film distance and the exposure time. The correct exposure for a particular application may be determined by a process of trial and error or by using an aid, such as an exposure chart, which relates to a specific grade of film. Often screens are used to improve contrast and reduce exposure times. A lead screen, which is a very thin film of lead bonded to thin card, is placed in contact with both sides of the radiographic film and serves two functions. It absorbs low-energy scattered radiation and interacts with incident high-energy radiation with a resulting emission of electrons. The emitted electrons activate the film emulsion giving improved developed film densities and enhanced contrast. Another type of intensifying screen is the fluorescent screen. Small crystals of calcium tungstate on a thin card base will fluoresce, emitting visible light, when subjected to radiation. They can intensify a radiographic image by a factor of up to 100, thus reducing exposure times, but they do not have a filtering effect on scattered radiation. A third type of screen is the fluoro-metallic screen, comprising both lead and fluorescent crystals, thus combining the advantages of both the former types.

It is necessary to identify radiographs so that a particular film can always be related to a particular test-piece, or portion of a test-piece and identification markers are used for this purpose. In addition to identification, each radiograph should contain some means of assessing the quality or sensitivity of the image. This is achieved using devices termed *Image Quality Indicators* or *penetrameters*. Identification markers are made of lead or lead alloy, usually in the form of letters and numbers. These are then attached to either the test piece or the film cassette by means of adhesive tape during the setting up process. The markers should be placed in such a way that they will not obscure any portion of the test-piece because the shadows of the dense metal characters would mask coincident defects. Several image quality indicators or penetrameters of different designs have been devised by the various standards organisations and they are generally made in the form of steps or wires of varying thickness and made in the same or a similar material to that being inspected. The relevant British Standard (BS 3971) covers both step-hole and wire IQI types, and these are shown in Figure 8.20. Step-hole IQIs to BS 3971 may be machined as a series of steps from a single plate or may be composed of a series of separate plaques mounted on plastic or rubber. A straight six-stage step-hole IQI is shown in Figure 8.20

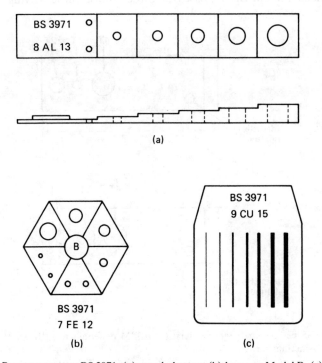

Figure 8.20 Penetrameters to BS 3971: (a) step-hole type; (b) hexagon Model B; (c) wire type.

(a) while Figure 8.20 (b) shows the Model B hexagonal IQI. Identification markers must be put on to indicate the type of material and the thickness range of the IQI. In Figure 8.20 (a) the coding 8 AL 13 indicates that the IQI is in aluminium with the thinnest step being No. 8 (0.630 mm) and the thickest step being No. 13 (2.00 mm) while in Figure 8.20 (b) the coding 7 FE 12 means that the IQI is in steel with step thicknesses ranging from No. 7 (0.500 mm) to No. 12 (1.60 mm). Figure 8.20 (c) shows an example of the wire type IQI conforming to BS 3971. A series of wires, each of 30 mm length are laid parallel and set 5 mm apart within an optically transparent material such as polythene. The lead identification markers are also encased with the polythene. In Figure 8.20 (c) the coding 9 CU 15 means that there are seven copper wires ranging in diameter from wire No. 9 (0.200 mm diam.) to wire No. 15 (0.80 mm diam.) With the aid of penetrameters, the image quality, or sensitivity, can be expressed as a percentage. The sensitivity is the thickness of the thinnest wire or step or hole visible in the developed radiograph expressed as a percentage of the thickness of the test-piece.

The types of penetrameter to meet US specifications differ from those specified in British Standards. Plaque type penetrameters, as illustrated in Figure 8.21, are used.

To satisfy the ASTM standard, a penetrameter as shown in Figure 8.21(a) is used. This is a thin plaque of a thickness (T) equal to a small percentage of the testpiece thickness. It possesses three holes, these having diameters

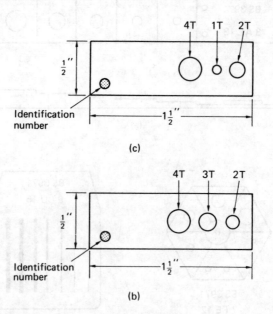

(c)

(b)

Figure 8.21 US plaque-type penetrameters: (a) ASTM penetrameter; (b) ASME penetrameter.

Table 8.4 Sensitivities of ASTM image quality levels

Image quality level	Penetrameter thickness (per cent of testpiece thickness)	Smallest visible hole size	Equivalent sensitivity (per cent)
1–1T	1	1T	0.7
1–2T	1	2T	1.0
2–1T	2	1T	1.4
2–2T	2	2T	2.0
2–4T	2	4T	2.8
4–2T	4	2T	4.0

equal to once, twice and four times the thickness of the penetrameter, subject to minimum hole diameters of 0.010 inch, 0.020 inch and 0.040 inch respectively. The ASME penetrameter (Figure 8.21(b)) is very similar with a thickness (T) equal to 2 per cent of the testpiece thickness and hole diameters of twice, three times and four times the penetrameter thickness, with a minimum hole diameter size of 0.068 inch. The identification number of an ASTM or ASME penetrameter is its thickness in thousands of an inch.

With the ASME standard, where the thickness of the penetrameter is 2 per cent of the testpiece thickness, if all three holes are visible on the developed film the sensitivity is equal to 2 per cent. In the ASTM system, image quality is rated by code symbols, 1-1T, 1-2T, 2-1T, and so on. The first figure in the code is the thickness of the penetrameter as a percentage of the test piece thickness and the last two characters represent the smallest hole size visible in the developed radiograph. The equivalent percentage sensitivities of these image qualities are given in Table 8.4.

The placement of penetrameters is important. They should be placed on the source side of the test-piece and at the edge of the area, namely in the outer zone of the radiation beam with the thinnest step or wire being outermost.

A radiograph is valueless unless the developed image can be sensibly interpreted, and correct interpretation needs a person who possesses a considerable amount of knowledge, skill and experience. The interpreter, therefore, needs to have a thorough knowledge of the principles of radiography and to be fully aware of the capabilities and the limitations of the techniques and equipment. In addition, the interpreter should have knowledge of the components to be inspected and the variables in the manufacturing processes which may give rise to defects. For example, in the inspection of castings, it would be beneficial if the interpreter is aware of the way in which effects such as gas porosity, shrinkage and cold shuts, can occur and the most likely areas in the particular casting where they may be found. The radiographic interpreter is looking for changes in image density in the radiograph. Density changes may be caused by one of three factors, namely a change in the thickness of the test-piece, including visible surface indentations or protuberances, internal flaws within the component, and density changes which may be induced by faulty processing, mishandling or bad film storage conditions. It is important that the interpreter can assess the nature and cause of each density difference observed. The conditions in which radiographs are viewed, therefore, are highly important, and the films should be correctly illuminated by means of a purpose-built light source which will give good illumination without glare or dazzle. The radiograph should be viewed in a darkened room so that there will be no light reflections from the surface of the film and the image is seen solely by means of light transmitted through the film. Viewing in poor conditions will cause rapid onset of eye fatigue and so it is also important that the interpreter is in a comfortable position and has no undue distractions. Ultimately, the efficiency of flaw detection is determined by the skill and experience of the interpreter and a highly-experienced radiograph interpreter may locate defect indications which could be missed by a less-experienced person.

8.21 The Radiation Hazard

X- and γ-radiation can cause damage to body tissue and blood, but any damage caused is not immediately apparent. The effects of any small doses of radiation received over a period of time is cumulative and so all workers who may be exposed to even small quantities of radiation should have a periodic blood count and medical examination.

Strict regulations cover the use of X- and γ-rays and the quantity of radiation to which workers may be exposed. The unit of quantity of X- or γ-radiation is the roentgen (see Section 8.19) which is based on the amount of ionisation caused in a gas by the radiation. The roentgen expresses a radiation quantity in terms of air rather than in terms of radiation absorbed by the human body. The unit which has been adopted for radiation absorbed by the body is the sievert (Sv) which is defined as an energy absorption of 1 joule per kilogramme. (Formerly the unit used was the rad (radiation absorbed dose), 1 Sv = 100 rad). The extent to which a gas is ionised by radiation can be determined by measuring the electrical conductivity of the gas and this principle is used in instruments for the measurement of radioactivity. For all practical purposes, the sievert, for X-rays and γ-rays with photon energies of less than 3 MeV, can be approximately equated with 100 roentgen. Medical authorities consider that there is a maximum permissible radiation dose which can be tolerated by the human body, and this dose is stated as being that amount of radiation which, *in the light of current knowledge*, will not cause appreciable harm to the body over a number of years. The currently accepted dose for classified workers, namely those who are engaged in radiography, is 1 mSv (0.1 rad) for a normal five-day working week and the maximum dosage rate for a year is 50 mSv (5 rad).

A fixed X-ray unit is usually housed in a laboratory and the walls of the laboratory are constructed in such a manner as to afford the necessary shielding. The United Kingdom regulations state that radiation on the outer side of the shielding should not exceed 7.5 μSv (0.75 millirad) per hour or, if only classified radiography workers have access to the area, should not exceed 25 μSv (2.5 millirad) per hour. The walls of an X-ray unit. therefore, are usually lined with a thickness of lead or made to have a high absorption factor using barium concrete. Any glazing will be of thick lead-silicate glass. The X-ray unit controls should be placed outside the shielded room.

There are many cases where the material to be radiographed is too large to be taken into an X-ray laboratory and radiography must be carried out on site, for example, in a workshop or aircraft hanger. In these cases, it is distance which will give the necessary protection and a sufficiently large area must be roped off and warning signs posted to keep all personnel outside the danger area.

The extent of radiation which may be received by classified workers in the field of radiography must be monitored and this is best achieved by recording the dosage received on a radiation monitoring film (film badge) or by using a pocket ionisation chamber. The film badge type of dosemeter consists of a small piece of film packed in a light-tight paper envelope and held within a small plastic container which is pinned or clipped to the operator's outer clothing. The film badge is carried by the operator for some predetermined time and is then processed under standardised conditions. The density of the processed film is compared with pieces of film of the same type and batch which have been exposed to known levels of radiation and processed under the same conditions. It is a statutory requirement in the United Kingdom that full records be kept of the radiation doses received by classified radiographic workers.

8.22 Advantages, Limitations and Applications of Radiography

Radiography is capable of detecting any feature in a component or structure provided that there are sufficient differences in thickness or density within the test piece. Large differences are more readily detected than small differences. The main types of defect which can be distinguished are porosity and other voids and inclusions, where the density of the inclusion differs from that of the basic material. Generally speaking, the best results will be obtained when the defect has an appreciable thickness in a direction parallel to the radiation beam. Plane defects such as cracks are not always detectable and the ability to locate a crack will depend upon its orientation to the beam. The sensitivity possible in radiography depends upon many factors but generally if a feature causes a change in absorption of 2 per cent or more, compared with the surrounding material then it will be detectable.

Radiography and ultrasonics are the two methods which are generally used for the successful detection of internal flaws that are located well below the surface, but neither method is restricted to the detection of this type of defect. The methods are complementary to one another in that radiography tends to be more effective when flaws are non-planar in type whereas ultrasonics tends to be more effective when the defects are planar. Radiographic inspection techniques are frequently used for the checking of welds and castings and, in many instances, radiography is specified for inspection of these components. This is the case for weldments and thick-wall castings which form part of high pressure systems. Radiography can also be used to inspect assemblies to check the condition and proper placement of components. One application for which radiography is very well suited is the inspection of electrical and electronic component assemblies to detect cracks, broken wires, missing or misplaced components and unsoldered connections. Radiography can be used to inspect most types of solid material but there could be problems with very high or very low density materials. Non-metallic and metallic materials, both ferrous and non-ferrous, can be radiographed and there is a fairly wide range of material thicknesses that can be inspected. The sensitivities of the radiography processes are affected by a number of factors including the type and geometry of the material and the type of flaw.

Although radiography is a very useful non-destructive test system it possesses some relatively unattractive features. It tends to be an expensive technique, compared with other non-destructive test methods. The capital costs of fixed X-ray equipment are high but, coupled with this, considerable space is needed for a radiography laboratory, including a dark room for film processing. Capital costs will be much less if portable X-ray sets or γ-ray sources are used for *in situ* inspections but space will still be required for film processing and interpretation. The operating costs for radiography are also high. The setting-up time for radiography is often lengthy and may account for over half of the total inspection time. Another aspect which adds to radiography costs is the need to protect personnel from the effect of radiation, and stringent safety precautions have to be employed. This safety aspect will apply to all who work in the vicinity of a radiography test as well as those persons directly concerned in the testing.

8.23 Self Assessment Questions

8.1 Give a brief description of the principles of penetrant inspection. What are the five essential stages in this type of inspection?

8.2 Why is it necessary to magnetise a component more than once for successful magnetic particle inspection?

8.3 What inspection technique could be used for the detection of surface defects if access to only a portion of a component surface is possible?

8.4 For what purposes other than the detection of defects can electrical test methods be used?

8.5 How does the type of material being tested and the type of defect being sought affect the choice of test frequency in eddy current inspection?

8.6 Why is it necessary to use a couplant between an ultrasonic probe and the material being tested?

8.7 How do changes in (a) the tube voltage and (b) the tube current affect the radiation emitted from an X-ray tube?

8.8 What is an Image Quality Indicator and for what reasons is it used?

Answers to Self Assessment Questions

Chapter 2

2.1 The load should be adjusted to give an impression with a diameter which lies between 0.25 and 0.5 of the diameter of the ball indentor if accurate hardness values are to be achieved.

2.2 The Vickers pyramidal diamond gives impressions which are always geometrically similar, irrespective of their depth. This is not true for impressions made by a ball indentor. The Brinell test is restricted to materials of low and medium hardness. With very hard materials, the ball indentor may deform. The diamond test can be used for all metals from the very soft to the extremely hard.

2.3 (a) $H_D = 1.854F/d^2 = (1.854 \times 2.5) / 0.362^2 = 35.4$, (b) $d = (1.854F)^{1/2} / H_D$ $= (1.854 \times 5)^{1/2} / 35.4 = 0.510\,mm$

2.4 There is not just one Rockwell scale of hardness but many, depending on the indentor/load combination used. Each scale gives hardness values in the range from 0 to 100. The hardness number must be qualified by a letter, A, B, C etc, to indicate the exact indentor/load combination used.

2.5 The Knoop diamond indentor gives a long but narrow indentation as opposed to the square indentation made by the Vickers diamond. In micro-hardness testing, the length of the Knoop impression can be measured with a greater accuracy than is possible for the diagonal length of the Vickers impression.

2.6 Each strike on the surface by the Shore falling weight will cause a small amount of plastic deformation with consequent work hardening of the material. Repeated strikes will give increasing hardness values.

2.7 Hardness tests are quick and relatively easy to carry out. They are not destructive and only cause small localised surface deformation. The hardness result can give an indication of the strength and ductility of the material and will also indicate if heat treatments have been carried out effectively.

2.8 Put the data in logarithmic form:

$F = 125$, $\ln F = 4.828$, $d = 2.20$, $\ln d = 0.788$
$F = 250$, $\ln F = 5.521$, $d = 2.70$, $\ln d = 0.993$
$F = 375$, $\ln F = 5.927$, $d = 3.10$, $\ln d = 1.131$

A plot of $\ln F$ against $\ln d$ gives a straight line with slope $= n = 3.2$. The intercept gives $\ln a = 2.3$, from which $a = 10$.

Chapter 3

3.1 The parameters which may be determined in a full tensile test are: Young's modulus (E), yield stress or proof stress, tensile strength, percentage elongation on gauge length and, for test-pieces of circular cross-section, percentage reduction in area.

3.2 A value of percentage elongation has little meaning unless the gauge length over which it was measured is quoted. For any material, the measured percentage elongation increases as the gauge length used decreases.

3.3 There are two main differences. Many thermoplastic materials are strain-rate sensitive and specified rates of strain must be used in standard test procedures. This does not apply to the testing of metals. Another difference is that, for metals, the percentage elongation value is obtained by piecing the broken test-piece together after the test and taking a measurement. In plastics testing, the distance between gauge marks is measured at the moment of fracture before elastic springback has occurred.

3.4 Plot the tabulated data as a graph of force against extension.

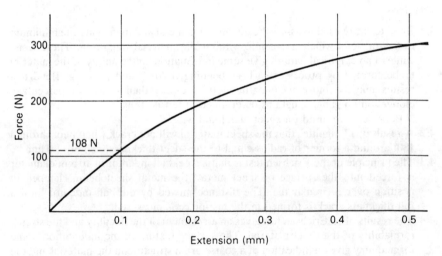

The graph shows no linear portion and is typical of a soft thermoplastic. To determine the secant modulus obtain the load which gives a strain of 0.2 per cent (0.2 per cent of 50 mm is 0.1 mm). From the graph, the load to give an extension of 0.1 mm is 108 N.

E = stress/strain = (force/cross-sectional area)/strain
  = $(108/12.61 \times 3.47)/0.002 = 1.23 \times 10^3$ N/mm^2 = 1.23 GN/m^2.

Tensile strength = maximum force/original cross-sectional area
  = $1290/12.61 \times 3.47 = 29.5$ N/mm^2 = 29.5 MN/m^2

Percentage elongation at break on 50 mm = $(97 - 50)/50 \times 100 = 94$ per cent

From the values calculated, the material is likely to be a soft thermoplastic, probably polyethylene or polypropylene.

3.5 The tensile strength of a brittle material may be determined by means of a three-point bend test to failure. The tensile strength measured in this way is also known as the modulus of rupture.

3.6 In a split cylinder test, tensile strength $= 2 F/\pi\, L\, D$. Tensile strength $= (2 \times 47.5 \times 10^3)/(\pi \times 0.1 \times 0.1) = 3.02 \times 10^6$ N/m^2.

3.7 The results of direct shear tests are qualitative rather than quantitative, but do give an indication of how a material may behave during production operations which involve shearing and blanking.

3.8 Brittle materials such as ceramics and concretes have tensile strengths which are very much less than their compressive strengths. There is less consistency in tensile strength results for these materials because of the presence of micro-cracks and other small defects always present to some extent.

Tensile tests are the most commonly used tests for metals and plastics because consistent results can be achieved.

Chapter 4

4.1 Bend tests are used to assess the ductility of a metal and to indicate the minimum radius of bend which is possible without the material fracturing. These tests, while of an empirical nature, give some information on the ability of the material to be formed by processes such as bending, folding and pressing. Bend test results may be more meaningful in this respect than values of percentage elongation on gauge length as determined in tensile tests.

Bend tests are used for sheet metal and wire.

4.2 A result of 1T signifies that the sheet material will not crack when bent through 180° around a former of radius equal to the sheet thickness, namely 1.3 mm.

4.3 The principle of the Erichsen test is that a steel ball indentor of 10 mm diameter is forced into the surface of sheet metal, the metal sheet being clamped in position over a circular die. The distance moved by the ball indentor until a full-thickness crack is formed in the test-piece is measured.

4.4 The results of an Erichsen test gives an assessment of the ductility and the stretch formability of the sheet material. The surface texture of the indentation dome formed may give an indication of a coarse grain structure in the material and the shape and direction of the crack formed will give information on anisotropy, or directionality, in the sheet metal.

4.5 The cupping coefficient, h^2/r^2, where h is the depth of indentation and r is the radius of curvature of the indentation, as determined in a Jovignot test, is a measure of the ductility and formability of sheet metal.

4.6 Cup draw tests can be used to assess the ability of sheet metal to be formed successfully by deep drawing or metal spinning operations. It will also give information on directionality in the sheet metal.

4.7 Ears are peaks around the circumference of a deep drawn cup (see Figure 4.6(c)). They are formed when sheet metal possessing a directional grain structure is deep drawn. The directionality, or anisotropy, in the sheet metal gives it a greater ductility in some directions than in others resulting in an uneven draw.

Chapter 5

5.1 A ductile failure is one which is preceded by a considerable amount of plastic deformation while in a brittle fracture there is little, if any, plastic deformation prior to failure.

5.2 One of the factors which affects the failure mode of many metals is temperature. Metals with a b.c.c. or c.p.h. crystal structure undergo a change from brittle to ductile behaviour as the temperature is raised. When metals of this type are subjected to impact loading, there is a sharp transition from a brittle cleavage fracture to a tough fibrous fracture over a narrow band of temperature as the temperature is raised. The transition temperature, as assessed from a series of notch-impact tests, is known as the notch-ductility transition temperature (NDTT). The value of the NDTT for low carbon and structural steels is dependent upon the composition of the steel and for many steels is between $-40\,°C$ and $+10\,°C$.

5.3 Notch-impact tests form a relatively cheap and easy way of revealing a tendency to brittleness in a material and they can be an effective means of checking whether or not heat treatments have been completed successfully. They provide the best means for determining the NDTT value for a metal also.

5.4 The time required to position a test-piece correctly within a Charpy machine is very much less than that required with the Izod machine. This makes the Charpy test much more suitable than the Izod method for testing metal samples at temperatures above or below ambient values.

5.5 Notch-impact test results should be expressed as energy for fracture per unit area of cross-section (kJ/m^2).

The effective cross-sectional area of the test-piece (area below the notch) is $10 \times 8 = 80$ mm^2. The notch impact value is $115/(80 \times 10^{-6}) = 1438$ kJ/m^2.

5.6 The term fracture toughness is the critical toughness of a material in relation to mode I opening of a crack in plane strain. K_{IC} (see Figure 5.6). Notch-impact toughness is energy required to fracture a test-piece using a high energy impact force in an Izod, Charpy or similar machine.

5.7 The fracture toughness parameters of a metal which plastically deforms as a crack grows are determined using a crack opening displacement (COD) test. A critical value of the crack opening displacement can be related to the fracture toughness of the material.

Chapter 6

6.1 Many steels show a definite fatigue limit. It is the maximum value of stress, in an alternating stress cycle, which can be applied without failure by fatigue occurring irrespective of the number of loading cycles used.

6.2 Peening of a surface induces residual compressive stresses in the surface layers of a component. Fatigue crack initiation and growth is mainly due to the action of tensile stresses. The introduction of residual compressive stress within the material will improve fatigue life.

6.3 Surface condition has a major influence on fatigue life. Surface roughness, incidental scratches and other surface imperfections can act as points of stress concentration. This is particularly so if they are transverse to the axis of direct stress. Fatigue test samples should have a polished surface with any grit lines from the final silicon carbide polishing paper being in the longitudinal direction.

6.4 Different answers will be obtained according to whether Goodman's, Gerber's or Soderberg's relationship is applied.

Using Goodman's equation: $\sigma_a = \sigma_{FL} \{1 - (\sigma_m/\sigma_{rs})\}$

$\sigma_a = 180 \{1 - (30/400)\} = 166.5$ MPa, so that the maximum permissible stress range will be from $(166.5 + 30)$ or 196.5 MPa in tension to $(30 - 166.5)$ or 136.5 MPa in compression.

Using Gerber's equation: $\sigma_a = \sigma_{FL} \{1 - (\sigma_m/\sigma_{rs})^2\}$

$\sigma_a = 180 \{1 - (30/400)^2\} = 179$ MPa, so that the maximum permissible stress range will be from 209 MPa in tension to 149 MPa in compression.

Using Soderberg's equation: $\sigma_a = \sigma_{FL} \{1 - (\sigma_m/\sigma_y)\}$

$\sigma_a = 180 \{1 - (30/320)\} = 163$ MPa, so that the maximum permissible stress range will be from 193 MPa in tension to 133 MPa in compression.

6.5 Any sharp change in cross-section or any geometric feature, such as a keyway will act as a stress raiser. The provision of adequate radiusing at such features to reduce the stress concentration effect will be beneficial in improving the fatigue life.

6.6 The Wöhler test is of the rotating beam type. The test-piece is mounted as a cantilever and a weight attached, via a ball-race, at the free end. When the specimen is rotated the stress in any surface element moves through an alternating cycle from tension through compression to tension again with a mean stress of zero.

6.7 Rotating beam fatigue tests are straightforward easy to conduct and the testing machines for these tests are of comparatively simple form and relatively inexpensive. The main disadvantage is that only alternating load cycles, with a zero value of mean stress, can be applied.

Chapter 7

7.1 Primary or transient creep is the first stage of creep during which an initial high rate of creep strain steadily reduces to a constant rate of creep strain. Secondary, or steady state, creep is the main stage during which the creep strain rate is constant. Eventually, there is a transition from the secondary into the tertiary stage. Localised necking of the material occurs and the rate of creep then increases and this leads to failure.

7.2 Relaxation is the reduction in the intensity of stress in a material with time when the strain is constant.

7.3 The quantitative information which may be derived from a tensile creep test is (a) the rate of strain during steady state creep, (b) the time at which tertiary creep begins, (c) the time at which final failure occurs and (d) the time required to produce some specified amount of strain.

7.4 At very high temperatures, close to the melting temperature of a material, creep is due to a viscous flow of grain boundary material. Single crystal components, with no grain boundaries, and directionally solidified components, with few grain boundaries in a transverse direction, show superior creep resistance to conventionally processed materials.

7.5 To comply with standards requirements, very close temperature control is necessary during creep testing. Thermocouples attached to a test-piece would, of necessity, be some little distance from the furnace windings and this would lead to delayed control response times.

7.6 Stress-rupture tests are used to determine the time to rupture only. It is not necessary to fit an extensometer to the test-piece and take readings at intervals during the test. Because of this, stress-rupture tests often involve using several test-pieces mounted in line as a string within the one creep test rig.

7.7 The total permissible strain is 2 mm on a 150 mm length, namely 2/150 or 0.0133. The design life is 15 000 hours, so the maximum creep strain rate which is acceptable is $0.0133/15\,000 = 8.89 \times 10^{-7}$/hour.

Chapter 8

8.1 Liquid penetrant inspection involves the absorption of a liquid into a surface-breaking defect and subsequent release of this liquid into an absorbent coating applied to the surface to give a visible indication of any such defect. To give good visibility, the penetrant liquid contains either a bright dye or a fluorescent chemical.

The five essential stages are:

(a) surface cleaning to remove oil, grease and other contaminants,
(b) penetrant application, allowing time for it to enter cracks,
(c) removal of excess penetrant,
(d) application of absorbent powder to develop and reveal defects,
(e) inspection (using ultraviolet light if a fluorescent penetrant is used).

8.2 The sensitivity and effectiveness of magnetic particle inspection depends upon the orientation of a defect to the induced magnetic field and will be greatest when the defect is normal to the field. It is necessary, therefore, to magnetise a component twice, in directions perpendicular to each other, for the successful indication of all detectable defects.

8.3 For this application, it would be possible to utilise Rayleigh, or surface, ultrasonic waves. A Rayleigh probe could be positioned on an accessible section of surface. The surface wave generated would be reflected by any surface defect in its path.

8.4 Electrical test methods can be used to measure physical properties, such as electrical conductivity, magnetic permeability and hardness, and to determine the thickness of surface coatings as well as to detect defects. Information on the physical properties can be used, in certain cases, to make deductions about heat treatment condition or crystal grain size, or used as a means of sorting materials.

8.5 As the test frequency is increased so the depth of penetration of the eddy current field decreases. The highest sensitivity for surface defect detection is obtained at the higher frequencies. When sub-surface defects are sought a low frequency is necessary, but sensitivities are diminished. Very low frequencies are needed for the inspection of ferro-magnetic materials because of the inherent small depth of eddy current penetration in these materials.

8.6 There is almost 100 per cent reflection of compression wave energy at an air/metal interface. When a high density fluid, such as oil or water, is used to couple a transducer crystal to a metal surface the amount of reflection will be reduced and a small proportion (about 6 per cent) of the incident sound energy will be transmitted into the metal.

8.7 (a) An increase in the voltage of an X-ray tube will increase the energies of the electrons striking the target and result in the production of higher energy X-ray photons. In other words, X-radiation of shorter wavelength and, hence, greater penetrating power will be generated. (b) An increase in the tube current will increase the number of electrons striking the target and will increase the intensity of the X-ray emission.

8.8 An Image Quality Indicator, or penetrameter, is used as a means of assessing the quality and sensitivity of radiographs. It may be either a metal plaque with several specific thicknesses or a series of wires of differing gauges mounted in a holder. It is placed on a component to be radiographed. When the developed radiograph is inspected the thinnest portion of the penetrameter visible indicates the minimum thickness defect which would be detectable in the radiograph. The thickness of the thinnest section of the penetrameter expressed as a percentage of the sectional thickness of the material radiographed is termed the sensitivity.

Appendix: Some Relevant British and American Standards

British		American (ASTM)	
Number	Title	Number	Title
General		E 6-89	Standard Terminology Relating to Methods of Mechanical Testing
Hardness Testing			
BS 240(1986)	Method for Brinell hardness test and for verification of Brinell hardness testing machines	E 10–84	Standard Test Method for Brinell Hardness of Metallic Materials
BS 427 Part 1(1981) Part 2(1990)	Method for Vickers hardness test Testing of metals Verification of the testing machine	E 92–82	Standard Test Method for Vickers Hardness of Metallic Materials
BS 891(1989)	Methods for hardness test (Rockwell method) and for verification of hardness testing machines (Rockwell method)	E 18–89a	Standard Test Methods Rockwell Hardness and Rockwell Superficial Hardness of Metallic Materials
BS 4175(1989)	Methods for superficial hardness test (Rockwell method) and for verification of superficial hardness testing machines (Rockwell method)		
BS 2782 Part 3 Method 365C (1986)	Determination of Rockwell hardness (plastics)	D 785–89	Standard Test Method for Rockwell Hardness of Plastics and Electrical Insulating Materials
BS 2782 Part 3 Method 365D (1983)	Determination of hardness of plastics and ebonite by the ball indentation method	E 448–82	Standard Practice for Scleroscope Hardness Testing of Metallic Materials

British		American (ASTM)	
Number	*Title*	*Number*	*Title*
BS 5441 Part 6 (1988)	Vickers and Knoop microhardness tests	E 384–89	Standard Test Method for Microhardness of Materials
		E 140–88	Standard Hardness Conversion Tables for Metals
BS 2782 Part 10 Method 1001 (1989)	Measurement of hardness by means of a Barcol impressor (reinforced plastics)	D 2583–87	Standard Test Method for Indentation Hardness of Rigid Plastics by means of a Barcol Impressor
		D 1415–88	Standard Test Method for Rubber Property – International Hardness
BS 2782 Part 3 Method 365B (1981)	Determination of indentation hardness by means of a Durometer (Shore harness)	D 2240–86	Standard Test Method for Rubber Property – Durometer Hardness

Tension and Compression Testing

British		American (ASTM)	
BS 18(1987)	Methods for tensile testing of metals (including aerospace materials)	E 8–89b E 8M–89b	Standard Test Methods of Tension Testing Metallic Materials
BS 1452(1990)	Specification for grey iron castings		
BS 2782 Part 3 Methods 320A–320F (1986)	Tensile strength, elongation and elastic modulus (plastics)	D 638–89 D–638M–89	Standard Test Method for Tensile Properties of Plastics
BS 2782 Part 3 Methods 326A–326C (1986)	Determination of tensile strength and elongation of plastic films	D 412–87	Standard Test Method for Rubber Properties in Tension
BS 2782 Part 10 Method 1003(1989)	Determination of tensile properties – reinforced plastics		
BS 1610(1985)	Materials testing machines and force verification equipment	E 4–89	Standard Practices for Load Verification of Testing Machines
BS 3846(1985)	Methods for calibration and grading of extensometers for testing of metals	E 83–85	Standard Practice for Verification and Classification of Extensometers
		E 9–89a	Standard Test Methods of Compression Testing of Metallic Materials at Room Temperature
BS 2782 Part 3 Method 345A (1979)	Determination of compressive properties (plastics) by deformation at constant rate	D 695–89 D 695M–89	Standard Test Method for Compressive Properties of Rigid Plastics

British		American (ASTM)	
Number	Title	Number	Title
BS 1881 Part 116(1983)	Method for determination of compressive strength of concrete cubes	C 39–86	Standard Test Method for Compressive Strength of Cylindrical Concrete Specimens
		C 873–85	Standard Test Method for Compressive Strength of Concrete Cylinders Cast in Place in Cylindrical Molds
BS 1881 Part 117(1983)	Method for determination of tensile splitting strength (concrete)	C 496–86	Standard Test Method for Splitting Tensile Strength of Cylindrical Concrete Specimens

Flexural, Bend and Shear Testing

British		American (ASTM)	
BS 2782 Part 3 Methods 340A & B (1989)	Determination of shear strength of (plastic) sheet material	E 143–87	Standard Test Method for Shear Modulus at Room Temperature
BS 2782 Part 3 Method 335A (1989)	Determination of flexural properties of rigid plastics	D 790–86 D 790M–86	Standard Test Methods for Flexural Properties of Unreinforced and Reinforced Plastics and Electrical Insulating Materials
BS 2782 Part 10 Method 1005(1989)	Determination of flexural properties (of reinforced plastics). Three-point method	C 293–79	Standard Test Method for Flexural Strength of Concrete (Using Simple Beam with Center-Point Loading)
BS 1881 Part 118(1983)	Method for determination of flexural strength for concrete	C 78–84	Standard Test Method for Flexural Strength of Concrete (Using Simple Beam with Third-Point Loading)
BS 1639(1989)	Methods for bend testing of metals	E 290–87	Standard Test Method for Semi-Guided Bend Test for Ductility of Metallic Materials
BS 3855(1989)	Method for modified Erichsen cupping test for sheet metal	E 643–84	Standard Test Method for Ball Punch Deformation of Metallic Sheet

Impact and Fracture Testing

British		American (ASTM)	
BS 131 Part 1 (1989)	The Izod impact test on metals	E 23–88	Standard Test Methods for Notched Bar Impact Testing of Metallic Materials
BS 2782 Part 3 Method 350 (1984)	Determination of Izod impact strength of rigid plastics materials	D 256–88	Standard Test Methods for Impact Resistance of Plastics and Electrical Insulating Materials
BS 131 Part 2 (1972)	The Charpy V-notch test on metals		

British		American (ASTM)	
Number	Title	Number	Title
BS 131 Part 3 (1982)	The Charpy U-notch test on metals		
BS 2782 Part 3 Method 359 (1984)	Determination of Charpy impact strength of rigid plastics materials		
BS 131 Part 4 (1972)	Calibration of pendulum impact testing machines		
		E 616–89	Standard Terminology Relating to Fracture Testing
BS 5447(1987)	Method for the plane-strain fracture toughness (K_{IC}) of metallic materials	E 399–83	Standard Test Method for Plane-Strain Fracture Toughness of Metallic Materials
BS 5762(1986)	Methods for crack opening displacement (COD) testing	E 1290–89	Standard Test Method for Crack-Tip Opening Displacement (CTOD) Fracture Toughness Measurement

Fatigue Testing

		E 1150–87	Standard Definitions of Terms Relating to Fatigue
BS3518	Methods of fatigue testing	E 466–82	Standard Practice for Conducting Constant Amplitude Axial Fatigue Tests of Metallic Materials
Part 1 (1984)	General principles	E 468–90	Standard Practice for Presentation of Constant Amplitude Axial Fatigue Test Results for Metallic Materials
Part 2 (1984)	Rotating bending fatigue tests		
Part 3 (1984)	Direct stress fatigue tests	E 467–76	Standard Practice for Verification of Constant Amplitude Dynamic Loads in an Axial Load Fatigue Testing Machine
Part 4 (1984)	Torsional stress fatigue tests		
		E 606–80	Standard Recommended Practice for Constant-Amplitude Low-Cycle Fatigue Testing

Creep and Relaxation Testing

BS 3500	Methods for creep and rupture testing of metals	E 139–83	Standard Practice for Conducting Creep, Creep–Rupture and Stress-Rupture Tests of Metallic Materials
Part 1 (1987)	Tensile rupture testing	D 2990–77	Standard Test Method for Tensile, Compressive and Flexural Creep and Creep-Rupture of Plastics
Part 3 (1987)	Tensile creep testing		

British		American (ASTM)	
Number	Title	Number	Title
Part 6 (1987)	Tensile stress relaxation testing	E 328–86	Standard Methods for Stress Relaxation Tests for Materials and Structures
		D 2991–84	Standard Practice for Testing Stress-Relaxation of Plastics

Non-destructive Testing

British		American (ASTM)	
BS 3683 Parts 1–5	Glossary of terms used in non-destructive testing	E 1316–90	Standard Terminology for Non-destructive Examination
BS 6443(1984)	Method for penetrant flaw detection Inspection Method	E 165–80	Standard Practice for Liquid Penetrant
Aero M39(1972)	Method for penetrant inspection of aerospace products	E 433–71	Standard Reference Photographs for Liquid Penetrant Inspection
PD 6513(1985)	A guide to the principles and practice of applying magnetic particle flaw detection	E 125–63	Standard Reference Photographs for Magnetic Particle Inspection
BS 6072(1986)	Method for magnetic particle flaw detection	E 709–80	Standard Practice for Magnetic Particle Examination
BS 4069(1982)	Specification for magnetic flaw detection inks and powders		
BS 3889	Methods for non-destructive testing of pipes and tubes	D 309–83	Standard Practice for Eddy-Current Examination of Steel Tubular Products using Magnetic Saturation
Part 2A(1986) Part 2B(1987)	Eddy current testing of wrought steel tubes		
	Eddy current testing of non-ferrous tubes	E 426–88	Standard Practice for Electromagnetic (Eddy-Current) Examination of Seamless and Welded Tubular Products. Austenitic Stainless Steel and Similar Alloys
		E 571–82	Standard Practice for Electromagnetic (Eddy-Current) Examination of Nickel and Nickel Alloy Tubular Products
		E 243–90	Standard Practice for Electromagnetic (Eddy–Current) Testing of Seamless Copper and Copper Alloy Tubes
		E 1004–84	Standard Test Method for Electromagnetic (Eddy-Current) Measurements of Electrical Conductivity

British		American (ASTM)	
Number	Title	Number	Title
BS 4331 Part 1 (1989)	Methods for assessing the performance characteristics of ultrasonic flaw detection equipment	E 213–86	Standard Practice for Ultrasonic Examination of Metal Pipe and Tubing
BS 3923(1983)	Methods for ultrasonic examination of welds	E–164–88	Standard Practice for Ultrasonic Contact Examination of Weldments
		E 587–82	Standard Practice for Ultrasonic Angle Beam Examination by the Contact Method
BS 2704(1983)	Specification for calibration blocks for use ultrasonic flaw detection	E 127–82a	Standard Practice for Fabricating and Checking Aluminium Alloy Ultrasonic Standard Reference Blocks
		E 428–71	Standard Practice for Fabrication and Control of Steel Reference Blocks used in Ultrasonic Inspection
Aero M34(1984)	Method of preparation and use of radiographic techniques	E 94–89	Guide for Radiographic Testing
BS 2600	Radiographic examination of fusion welded butt joints in steel	E 1032–85	Standard Method for Radiographic Examination of Weldments
BS 2910(1986)	Method for radiographic examination of fusion welded circumferential butt joints in steel pipes	E 1030–90	Standard Test Method for Radiographic Examination of Metallic Castings
BS 3971(1985)	Specification for image quality indicators for industrial radiography	E 142–86	Standard Method for Controlling Quality of Raidographic Testing
BS 5650(1978)	Specification for apparatus for gamma radiography	E 747–90	Standard Test Method for Controlling Quality of Radiographic Examination using Wire Penetrameters
		E 1025–89	Standard Practice for Hole-Type Image Quality Indicators used for Radiography

Index